BOOLEAN ALGEBRA

AND ITS APPLICATIONS

This book is in the

ADDISON-WESLEY SERIES IN THE
ENGINEERING SCIENCES

Electrical and Control Systems

BOOLEAN ALGEBRA
AND ITS APPLICATIONS

---

by

J. ELDON WHITESITT

Department of Mathematics
Montana State College

ADDISON-WESLEY PUBLISHING COMPANY, INC.

READING, MASSACHUSETTS, U.S.A.

LONDON, ENGLAND

PREFACE

George Boole (1815–1864) introduced in his book *The Laws of Thought* the first systematic treatment of logic and developed for this purpose the algebraic system now known by his name, Boolean algebra. Few mathematical works of the past 100 years have had a greater impact upon mathematics and philosophy than this famous book. The significance of the work has been well expressed by Augustus De Morgan:

> That the symbolic processes of algebra, invented as tools of numerical calculation, should be competent to express every act of thought, and to furnish the grammar and dictionary of an all-containing system of logic, would not have been believed until it was proved in *Laws of Thought*.

In addition to its applications in the field of logic, Boolean algebra has two other important applications. The first of these arises from the fact that Boolean algebra is the natural algebra with which to treat the combination of sets of elements under the operations of intersection and union of sets. With the addition of the idea of "number of elements" in a set, Boolean algebra becomes the foundation for the theory of probability. The algebra of sets is also important in many other branches of mathematics.

With the publication of two papers approximately 20 years ago, Claude E. Shannon introduced a new area of application of Boolean algebra when he showed that the basic properties of series and parallel combinations of bistable electrical devices such as relays could be adequately represented by this algebra. Since this time, Boolean algebra has played a significant role in the important and complicated task of designing telephone switching circuits, automatic control devices, and electronic computers. At the present time, more interest is centered in this application than in either of the others.

This book, designed to be used as a text in a one-semester or two-quarter course, has developed out of notes used in such a course at Montana State College for the past two years. It is not possible, in a single book, to give an exhaustive account of Boolean algebra and all of its applications. The purpose of this book is to introduce the subject on a level which will make it available even to those with rather limited mathematical background, and to examine each of the applications in enough detail so that the student will gain an appreciation of the scope and usefulness of the subject. This book could well serve as a background for specialized courses in any of the major areas of application.

The first chapter deals with the algebra of sets from an intuitive point of view, since it is felt that this application is the most readily understood with little formal training. While this approach is less satisfying to the mathematically mature than an axiomatic treatment might be, it is hoped that this section will serve as motivation for the precise development of the subject which follows in Chapter 2. In Chapter 2, Boolean algebra is presented formally as an abstract algebraic system with no reference to applications. For many students this will be their first introduction to modern mathematics, and the training in the axiomatic method will be of value in any future work in mathematics.

Chapter 3 introduces symbolic logic, with special emphasis on those portions of logic which depend heavily upon the algebra of propositions, a Boolean algebra. In addition to extending the area of application of Boolean algebra, this chapter emphasizes those topics of logic most often used in elementary mathematics. The concepts of valid argument and indirect proofs are discussed in some detail.

Chapters 4, 5, and 6 are closely related and all deal with the third application of Boolean algebra mentioned, the algebra of circuits. Switching circuits are discussed in Chapter 4 as the most easily understood of the many types of circuits which can be treated. In Chapter 5 the ideas are extended to relay circuits which, although similar in principle, are much more versatile in applications. Finally, Chapter 6 discusses briefly some of the arithmetic circuits used by modern computers. Here the emphasis is on logical design rather than on the physical properties of components.

Chapter 7 is added for the benefit of those who would like to pursue the algebra of sets a little further, to an application in probability theory. While the treatment is brief, many fundamental concepts of probability are introduced and the basic dependence of probability upon the algebra of sets is clearly shown.

Since no notation is standard throughout all three applications of Boolean algebra, the notation used in this book was chosen on the basis of simplicity and ease of manipulation. Skill in the correct algebraic manipulation of the symbols is essential for the applications, and it is hoped that the use throughout of a single notational system will speed the process of acquiring this skill. The notation used is that commonly used in treatises on logical design of circuits, but will serve equally well for the other applications.

A short list of references is given at the end of each chapter. Students should be encouraged to do outside reading on topics of particular interest, either in these suggested texts or in current periodicals.

I would like to express appreciation to John W. Hurst, Head of the Department of Mathematics, Montana State College, for his encourage-

ment and for providing the opportunity to use this material in the class-
room in its various stages of development.   Thanks are due also to Mrs.
Janet Bierrum for her skillful help with typing and the preparation of the
manuscript.

Finally, I dedicate this book to my wife, Doris Whitesitt, for her understanding patience during the time of its preparation.

Montana State College   J. E. W.
March 1960

CONTENTS

ix

CHAPTER 1

THE ALGEBRA OF SETS

1–1 Introduction. Boolean algebra, as the name suggests, is part of that branch of mathematics known as modern algebra, or abstract algebra. It is one of the most easily understood of the algebraic systems usually studied in a basic course in algebra because of its simplicity and because of the readily available applications to illustrate the theory. No particular subject matter is prerequisite to the study of this text, although any maturity gained in other mathematics courses will be helpful.

In order to present Boolean algebra in a way which can be readily followed by a beginner, this chapter deals only with one of the special examples of a Boolean algebra, the algebra of sets. This example was chosen because it is perhaps the most intuitive of all applications and because at the same time it is complex enough to reveal the essential nature of any Boolean algebra. The development is entirely intuitive, in that any proofs given are based on intuitive concepts rather than on formal axioms. The axiomatic approach is delayed until Chapter 2. While this order is perhaps less satisfying to a professional mathematician, it is hoped that a greater appreciation of the precise formulation will result because the reader is already familiar with the properties represented in the axioms.

1–2 Element and set. Throughout mathematics there are countless instances where the concepts of "element" and "set of elements" (or class) play a crucial role. Every freshman student in mathematics is familiar with the set of integers, the set of all right triangles, the set of lines perpendicular to a given plane, and the set of points on a line. The concept of set is not limited to mathematics, however. The totality of books in a library, of people in a room, and of fish in a given stream are examples of sets. The purpose of this chapter is to investigate the nature of sets and the ways in which they may be combined. That sets obey laws of algebra similar, although not identical, to the laws of algebra for real numbers may seem strange at first. However, it will be shown how this phenomenon is a natural and very useful one.

In any subject in mathematics there are certain terms so basic that definition is impossible. In plane geometry, the terms *point* and *line* are undefined, although a student of geometry is encouraged to form an intuitive notion of the meaning of these words. We will take as undefined terms for the algebra of sets the words *element* and *set*. Intuitively we think

1

of elements as the basic objects which, in collections, constitute sets. As symbols we shall use the letters of the alphabet in lower case italics (a, b, c, x, y, etc.) to represent elements, and capital letters (A, B, X, etc.) to represent sets. A further symbol, $\in$, will be used to denote an undefined relation which may or may not hold between a particular element and a particular set, in that order. We may write, for example, $m \in X$, and read this symbol "m is a member of the set X." It will be assumed that for each element m and each set X in any discussion it is possible to determine whether or not the relation $m \in X$ is valid.

We will say that set X *equals* set Y, and write $X = Y$, if and only if the two sets are identical, that is, contain exactly the same elements. If a set X consists entirely of elements which are members of a second set Y, we say that X is a *subset* of Y and write $X \subseteq Y$. If, in addition, Y contains one or more elements not in X, we say X is a *proper subset* of Y.

It is convenient to introduce names for two special sets which will be important in any application. The first is called the *universal set* and is defined to be the set consisting of all elements under discussion. This set is also referred to as the domain of discourse, or the fundamental domain. The universal set will be denoted by the symbol 1. We note that every set is a subset of the universal set. The second special set, called the *null set*, is defined to be a set containing no elements at all. By definition, the null set is a subset of every other set. The notation for the null set will be the symbol 0. It is important to note that 0 and 1, as used here, are not numbers but the names of two special sets.

The algebra that will be developed is an algebra for sets, not for elements of sets. For example, the symbol $m \in X$ cannot be introduced into the algebra. It is frequently important to work with individual elements of sets, and since we cannot handle elements as such in the algebra, it is convenient to introduce the concept of a unit set. A *unit set* is a set which consists of a single element, and if this element is, say, x, we denote the set by $\{x\}$. In other instances as well, if the set is specified by listing each of the elements in the set, the symbol $\{\ \}$ will be used. For example, $\{a, b, c\}$ is understood to be the set consisting of the elements a, b, and c only.

Associated with each set X is another set X' called the *complement* of X and defined to be the set consisting of all elements of the universal set which are not elements of X. As special cases we note that the null set and the universal set are each complements of the other.

EXAMPLE. Consider a stack of books of which some are bound in red, some in black, and the rest in yellow. Suppose that all red books and some of the black books are written in English. The remainder of the black books are in German, and the yellow books are written in French. Let the set of all books in the stack be the universal set and let other sets be denoted as follows:

R is the set of red books,
Y is the set of yellow books,
B is the set of black books,
E is the set of books written in English,
F is the set of books written in French,
G is the set of books written in German.

In this example, $Y = F$ and $R \subseteq E$. In fact, R is a proper subset of E. If a particular red book is denoted by m, we may write $m \in R$ and also $m \in E$. Or we could write $\{m\} \subseteq R$ and $\{m\} \subseteq E$. E' is the set consisting of all yellow books and those black books which are written in German.

Exercises

1. List all subsets of the set $\{a, b, c\}$. (There are eight subsets, of which seven are proper subsets, counting the null set.)

2. Use the definition of complement to prove that $(X')' = X$ for any set X.

3. Describe the complement of each set of books given in the example of this section.

4. How many different subsets are there for a set containing a finite number n of elements? [*Hint:* Express the number of subsets with u elements, $u \leq n$, as a combinatorial symbol and use the binomial theorem to sum from 0 to n.]

1–3 The combination of sets. In this section we will investigate the rules by which sets may be combined to form new sets. First, for arbitrary sets X and Y, the *union* of X and Y is defined to be the set consisting of all elements which are either in X or in Y or in both X and Y. This new set is denoted by $X + Y$. In the illustration of Section 1–2 for example, $R + Y$ is the set of all red and all yellow books, $Y + E + G$ is the universal set of all books in the stack, and $R + E$ is just E, the set of all books written in English.

Next, the *intersection* of X and Y, for arbitrary sets X and Y, is defined to be the set consisting of those elements which are both in X and in Y. The intersection of X and Y will be denoted by XY, or by $X \cdot Y$. We will refer to the centered dot ($\cdot$) whenever it is desired to discuss the process of forming an intersection, just as the symbol ($+$) will refer to the process of forming the union of sets. For convenience the centered dot is usually omitted in algebraic expressions, as is common in the algebra of numbers. Again referring to the example of Section 1–2, we note that EB is the set of black books written in English, RY is the null set, and RE is R, the set of red books.

As immediate consequences of the definitions of ($+$), ($\cdot$), and ($'$), we note that for an arbitrary set X, $X + X' = 1$ and $XX' = 0$. The following theorem also comes directly from these definitions.

THEOREM. If m is any element in the universal set and X and Y are arbitrary sets, then m is a member of one and only one of the sets XY, XY', $X'Y$, and $X'Y'$.

Proof. By the definition of complement, m is an element of either X or X' but not both. If it happens that $m \in X$, then since m is an element of either Y or Y' but not both, m is a member of XY or XY' but not both, by definition of intersection. Similarly, if m is a member of X', then m is a member of $X'Y$ or $X'Y'$ but not both, which completes the proof.

The operations just defined are not independent of the symbols and relations defined in Section 1–2. A little reflection will reveal that the five conditions $X \subseteq Y$, $XY = X$, $X + Y = Y$, $XY' = 0$, and $X' + Y = 1$ all represent the same condition on the sets X and Y, namely, that each element of the set X is a member of the set Y. Again, the set $X + Y$ may be written $(X'Y')'$. These relationships simply illustrate the fact that we have introduced more symbols than are really necessary to treat the algebra of sets. The significance of this fact will be examined more closely in a later section. In the meantime, we will find it convenient to use all these symbols.

The symbols used in this chapter for intersection, union, and complementation are by no means standard. It was considered desirable to use a single notation throughout the text for the several applications of Boolean algebra. The set chosen is the one most commonly used in the application to circuit algebra. The notations most commonly used in other books are listed in the following table.

SYMBOLS IN COMMON USAGE

Meaning	*Symbolic notation*
Union of set X and set Y	$X + Y$, $X \cup Y$, $X \vee Y$
Intersection of set X and set Y	XY, $X \cap Y$, $X \wedge Y$
Complement of set X	X', $\overline{X}$, $\sim X$

EXERCISES

1. Refer to the Example in Section 1–2 and describe simply, in words, the following sets:

(a) $Y + G$ (b) RB' (c) $G(B + R)$ (d) $B + BR$

2. Justify for the Example in Section 1–2 that

(a) $(G + R)' = G'R'$ (b) $(GB)' = G' + B'$

3. Decide intuitively which of the following are always true for arbitrary sets X, Y, and Z. Do not give proofs.

(a) $X + XY = X$ (b) $X(X + Y) = X$
(c) $X(Y + Z) = XY + XZ$ (d) $X + YZ = (X + Y)(X + Z)$

4. If it is known that an element m is neither a member of the set X nor of the set Y', then describe the set to which m must belong. Write the symbolic expression for this set.

5. Let the universal set be the set of all positive integers and define sets S, E, and M as follows:

S is the set of all positive integers less than or equal to 6.

E is the set of all positive integers which are even, 2, 4, 6, etc.

M is the set of all positive integers which are multiples of 3, that is, 3, 6, 9, etc.

Write simple algebraic expressions in terms of S, E, and M for the following sets:

   (a) {3, 6}   (b) {1, 3, 5}
   (c) All positive integers which are multiples of 6.
   (d) All even integers greater than 6.
   (e) The set which contains all multiples of 3 and all odd integers.

1–4 Venn diagrams. A formal presentation of Boolean algebra, which will be given in Chapter 2, begins with a description of the symbols to be used and a statement of the axioms which it is assumed the symbols satisfy. Upon this foundation, a framework of theorems and definitions is constructed which becomes a mathematical model to be used in any application which the model seems to fit. The validity of the results obtained from the application depend upon the closeness with which the model fits the practical situation.

In Chapter 1, however, a different approach to Boolean algebra has been adopted. An application has been considered first, with the hope that the reading will be more pleasant and to provide a strong motivation for the axiomatic treatment to follow. This approach has its weaknesses, of course. The greatest is that we have no formal basis upon which to build precise proofs. Since there are no axioms to employ in writing proofs, we must rely upon an intuitive notion of the meanings of terms like "set" and "element." To strengthen this intuition and provide some justification for the basic laws which are valid in the algebra of sets, we shall introduce the concept of a *Venn diagram*. It should be remembered that such diagrams do not constitute proofs, but rather represent illustrations which make the laws seem plausible.

In a Venn diagram the set of points interior to a rectangle is taken as the universal set. Arbitrary sets within the universal set are represented by the sets of points interior to circles (or other closed regions) within the rectangle. If nothing specific is known about the sets involved, these circles are drawn so that all the possibilities of intersections among the sets are represented. By shading appropriate areas, all combinations of the sets can be represented graphically.

As an illustration of the usefulness of Venn diagrams, consider Fig. 1–1, representing two sets X and Y which have a nonzero intersection. In this

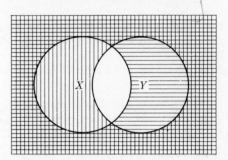

FIG. 1-1. A Venn diagram involving sets X and Y.

figure X', the complement of set X, is shaded with horizontal lines, and Y' is shaded with vertical lines. The set $X'Y'$ appears as the crosshatched area, which is clearly the complement of $X + Y$. Thus we have illustrated a basic law, that $(X + Y)' = X'Y'$. In the figure, the unshaded area represents XY, which is clearly the complement of $X' + Y'$, the area shaded either with horizontal lines, or vertical lines, or both. This illustrates a second basic law, namely, that $(XY)' = X' + Y'$.

As another illustration, consider Fig. 1-2, which illustrates the law $X + YZ = (X + Y)(X + Z)$. This diagram is constructed in steps to show more clearly how the required sets are determined. The diagrams are self-explanatory.

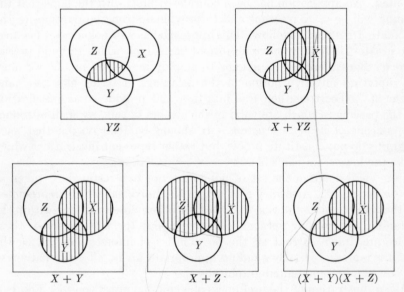

FIG. 1-2. Venn diagrams for the law $X + YZ = (X + Y)(X + Z)$.

EXERCISES

1. Draw a Venn diagram showing three sets X, Y, and Z with the maximum number of nonzero intersections and label each of the areas representing the sets XYZ, XYZ', $XY'Z$, $X'YZ$, $XY'Z'$, $X'YZ'$, $X'Y'Z$, $X'Y'Z'$.

2. Draw an appropriate Venn diagram for each of the following. Shade the indicated area.

(a) $X + X'YZ$

(b) $(X + Y')(X' + Y)$

(c) $(X + Y')(X' + Z)$

(d) $XY + XZ + YZ$

3. Use Venn diagrams to decide which of the following are valid for all sets X, Y, and Z.

(a) $X(Y + Z) = XY + XZ$

(b) $XY + X'Y + XY' = 1$

(c) $X(X + Y) = X$

(d) $X + XY = X$

(e) $X' + Y' = (X + Y)'$

(f) $X + X' = 1$

(g) $X + X'Y = X + Y$

(h) $X'Y' + X'Y + XY' = 1$

(i) $(X + Y)(X' + Z) = XZ + X'Y$

(j) $(XY)' = X'Y'$

4. Use Venn diagrams to determine simpler algebraic expressions for the following sets:

(a) $(XY + X'Y + XY')'$

(b) $[X'(Y + Z)]'$

(c) $(X + Y')(X' + Z)(Y + Z')$

(d) $XY + X'Z + YZ$

1–5 Fundamental laws. In Section 1–4 some of the basic identities which are valid in the algebra of sets (and in any Boolean algebra) were mentioned in connection with Venn diagrams. These laws and others which will be used throughout this book are listed below. The laws are numbered, for convenience of reference. The names given are those commonly used, although some of the names reflect one particular application, rather than Boolean algebra in general. For example, "complementation" suggests the application to algebra of sets, whereas "tautology" suggests the application to symbolic logic. No proofs for these laws are given, but each may be justified intuitively by the use of an appropriate Venn diagram.

If 1 denotes the universal set and 0 denotes the null set, the following identities are valid in the algebra of sets for arbitrary sets X, Y, and Z:

COMMUTATIVE LAWS

(1a) $XY = YX$

(1b) $X + Y = Y + X$

ASSOCIATIVE LAWS

(2a) $X(YZ) = (XY)Z$

(2b) $X + (Y + Z) = (X + Y) + Z$

DISTRIBUTIVE LAWS

(3a) $X(Y + Z) = XY + XZ$ (3b) $X + YZ = (X + Y)(X + Z)$

LAWS OF TAUTOLOGY

(4a) $XX = X$ (4b) $X + X = X$

LAWS OF ABSORPTION

(5a) $X(X + Y) = X$ (5b) $X + XY = X$

LAWS OF COMPLEMENTATION

(6a) $XX' = 0$ (6b) $X + X' = 1$

LAW OF DOUBLE COMPLEMENTATION

(7) $(X')' = X$

LAWS OF DE MORGAN

(8a) $(XY)' = X' + Y'$ (8b) $(X + Y)' = X'Y'$

OPERATIONS WITH 0 AND 1

(9a) $0X = 0$ (9b) $1 + X = 1$
(10a) $1X = X$ (10b) $0 + X = X$
(11a) $0' = 1$ (11b) $1' = 0$

Note that many of these laws are already familiar as laws which hold in the algebra of real numbers. However, (3b), (4a), (4b), (5a), and (5b) are not valid for numbers, and laws involving complementation obviously do not apply to numbers. It is perhaps surprising that any similarity at all is evident. Since some similarity does exist, it is especially important to study the ways in which this algebra differs from ordinary algebra. Among the differences is the fact that expressions such as $2X$ and X^2 will never appear in the algebra of sets. The laws of tautology make such expressions unnecessary. An interesting and useful property of Boolean algebra is the *principle of duality*. An examination of the laws will show that if, in any identity, each union is replaced by intersection, each intersection by union, 0 by 1, and 1 by 0, the resulting equation is also an identity. This rule holds generally in the algebra of sets and, as we shall see in Chapter 2, in any Boolean algebra.

EXERCISES

1. Check the validity of each of the fundamental laws by drawing the appropriate Venn diagram, unless the law was checked in Section 1–4.

1–6 Expanding, factoring, and simplifying. A *monomial* is defined to be either a single letter representing a set, with or without a prime, or an indicated product of two or more such symbols representing the intersection of these sets; X, Y', and $XY'Z$ are examples of monomials. A *polynomial* is an indicated sum of monomials, each of which is called a *term* of the polynomial. The polynomial represents the union of the sets corresponding to the separate terms; $X + Y' + XY'Z$ is an example of a polynomial. In any expression representing an intersection of sets, each such set will be termed a *factor* of the set of intersection. The factors of the set $X'(Y + Z)$ are X' and $Y + Z$. In particular, a factor is said to be *linear* if it is a single letter, with or without a prime, or a sum of such symbols: $X + Y'$ is linear, while $Z + XY$ and $(X + Y)'$ are not linear. In general, all useful terminology from the algebra of numbers will be carried over to the algebra of sets.

Many algebraic expressions arising in the algebra of sets lend themselves to remarkable simplifications. One may perform the usual operations of factoring, or expanding products, familiar from working with numbers, in any expression. These processes are based on applications of the first distributive law, number (3a), and are illustrated in the following examples.

EXAMPLE 1. Expand $(X + Y)(Z' + W)$ into a polynomial.

Solution. The steps in the expansion are as follows:

$$\begin{aligned}
(X + Y)(Z' + W) &= (X + Y)Z' + (X + Y)W & \text{by (3a)} \\
&= Z'(X + Y) + W(X + Y) & \text{by (1a)} \\
&= Z'X + Z'Y + WX + WY & \text{by (3a)}
\end{aligned}$$

It should be clear that from the commutative, associative, and the first distributive laws follows the method of expanding by inspection that one normally uses in the algebra of numbers. That is, in the above example, the final result may be written at once by merely forming all possible products of terms in the left factor by terms in the right factor.

EXAMPLE 2. Factor the polynomial $AC + AD + BC + BC$ into linear factors.

Solution. $\begin{aligned}[t] AC + AD + BC + BD &= A(C + D) + B(C + D) & \text{by (3a)} \\
&= (A + B)(C + D) & \text{by (1a) and (3a)} \end{aligned}$

In Example 2, the factoring was performed exactly as in the algebra of numbers, using law (3a). The algebra of sets differs from the algebra of numbers, however, in that every expression can be factored into linear factors. Law (3a) alone is not usually sufficient for this purpose. It can be shown, although the proof is not included here, that any expression may be factored into linear factors by repeated application of the second distributive law, number (3b). The next example illustrates the method and suggests how such a proof could be constructed.

EXAMPLE 3. Factor $XY + ZW$ into linear factors.

Solution.
$$\begin{aligned} XY + ZW &= (XY + Z)(XY + W) && \text{by (3b)} \\ &= (Z + XY)(W + XY) && \text{by (1b)} \\ &= (Z + X)(Z + Y)(W + X)(W + Y) && \text{by (3b)} \end{aligned}$$

If this factoring process is compared with the expansion in Example 1, it is evident that factoring can be done by inspection by a procedure which is dual to the procedure for expanding products. To factor a sum of two monomials, linear factors, consisting of sums in which one term is taken from the first monomial and the other from the second monomial, are formed in all possible ways. This process can be extended to sums of three or more monomials. With a little practice, factoring should become as easy as expanding products.

In addition to the processes of expanding and factoring, either of which may lead to simplifications of a given expression, there are several other laws, peculiar to Boolean algebra, which are highly useful. In particular, laws (4a), (4b), (5a), (5b), and (6a), (6b), when applicable, often result in striking simplifications. While no single example is likely to illustrate all possible uses of these laws, the following gives an indication of the kind of simplifications that can be made. These laws should be studied carefully in order to note other possibilities; they will prove useful in connection with working the problems on simplification.

EXAMPLE 4. Simplify the expression $X(X' + Y) + Y(Y + Z) + Y$.

Solution.
$$\begin{aligned} X(X' + Y) + Y(Y + Z) + Y &= XX' + XY + Y(Y + Z) + Y && \text{by (3a)} \\ &= 0 + XY + Y(Y + Z) + Y && \text{by (6a)} \\ &= XY + Y(Y + Z) + Y && \text{by (10b)} \\ &= XY + Y + Y && \text{by (5a)} \\ &= XY + Y && \text{by (4b)} \\ &= Y. && \text{by (5b)} \end{aligned}$$

Another identity not usually listed as a basic law applies so often to the problem of simplification that it is worth special mention. It is given in the following theorem.

THEOREM. For any sets X and Y, $X + X'Y = X + Y$.

Proof.
$$\begin{aligned} X + X'Y &= (X + X')(X + Y) && \text{by (3b)} \\ &= 1(X + Y) && \text{by (6b)} \\ &= X + Y. && \text{by (10a)} \end{aligned}$$

It is not always clear which form of an algebraic expression should be considered simplest. As an arbitrary rule, we will agree to consider as the *simplest form* for an algebraic expression, that form which requires use of the least number of symbols. We will count each instance of an operation of intersection, union, or complementation as a symbol. Each letter representing a set and each pair of parentheses will also count as a symbol. Thus $X(Y + Z')$ contains seven symbols and $XY + YZ'$ contains eight symbols, and hence the first form is considered simpler than the second.

A final comment on the problem of simplifying an expression concerns the use of De Morgan's laws. In an expression where a prime appears outside a parenthesis or other grouping symbol, it is usually necessary to apply either (8a) or (8b), as in Example 5 below. These laws may be easily extended to apply to a sum (or product) of three or more terms. For instance,

$$(A + B + C)' = [(A + B) + C]' = (A + B)'C' = A'B'C',$$

and similarly,

$$(ABC)' = A' + B' + C'.$$

EXAMPLE 5. Simplify $(AB + AC + A'X'Y)(AB'C + A'X'Y' + A'BY)'$.

Solution. (Reasons for each step should be supplied by the reader.)

$(AB + AC + A'X'Y)(AB'C + A'X'Y' + A'BY)'$
$\quad = (AB + AC + A'X'Y)(AB'C)'(A'X'Y')'(A'BY)'$
$\quad = (AB + AC + A'X'Y)(A' + B + C')(A + X + Y)(A + B' + Y')$
$\quad = (A'X'Y + AB + ABC + A'BX'Y + ABC' + A'C'X'Y)$
$\quad\quad\quad\quad\quad\quad \times (A + AX + B'X + XY' + AY + B'Y)$
$\quad = AB + A'B'X'Y + ABXY'$
$\quad = AB + A'B'X'Y.$

EXERCISES

1. Expand the following into a polynomial having as few terms as possible:

(a) $(X + Y'X)(X + YZ)$
(b) $(X + Y)(X' + Y)(X + Y')(X' + Y')$
(c) $(XY' + YZ)(X'Y' + XZ + YZ)$
(d) $(A + B + C' + A'X)[AC'(B' + X')]'$

2. Factor the following into linear factors:

(a) $X + Y'Z$ (b) $XY + ZW$ (c) $X + Y(Z + W)$
(d) $XY' + X'(Y + Z)$ (e) $AX' + AY(X + Z)$ (f) $ABC + A'D$

3. Simplify the following. (Each expression reduces to a single symbol.)

(a) $AB'A'B'$ (b) $AB + AB' + A'B + A'B'$
(c) $AC' + ABC + AC$ (d) $ABC + A' + B' + C'$ (cont.)

(e) $(A + B)(A' + B)$ (f) $(A + AB + ABC)(A + B + C)$

(g) $(AB' + A'B)'(AB + A'B')'$

(h) $ABC + ABC' + AB'C + A'BC + AB'C' + A'BC' + A'B'C + A'B'C'$

4. Simplify the following:

(a) $(AB + AB' + A'B')'$ (b) $(A + B' + C)(AB + A'C')'$

(c) $A'C + B'C + ABCD'$

(d) $(XY + XY' + X'Y)'(X'Y' + ZW)$

(e) $(A'BC')'(AB'C')'$ (f) $XY(XZ' + XY + XYZ)$

(g) $(XY + ABC)(XY + A' + B' + C')$

(h) $ABX + AB'X + X'ABX$

(i) $(XY + XY' + X'Y)(X + Y + Z + X'Y'Z')$

(j) $(XY + X'Y' + XY')'[(X' + Y')(X + Y')]'$

1–7 Properties of set inclusion. In Section 1–2, the notation $A \subseteq B$ was defined to mean that set A is contained within set B. When we wish to refer to the symbol $\subseteq$ without specific reference to any sets, we call it *set inclusion* just as $(+)$ is referred to as union. The laws in Section 1–5 refer only to intersection, union, and complementation. Set inclusion also satisfies some basic laws which are interesting and useful. These laws can be verified directly from the definition or by making use of Venn diagrams. Still another approach is to make use of the fact pointed out in Section 1–3 that $X \subseteq Y$ if and only if $XY' = 0$. The proofs given here are based on the definition of $\subseteq$.

THEOREM 1. If $X \subseteq Y$ and $Y \subseteq Z$, then $X \subseteq Z$. (This is known as the transitive property of inclusion.)

Proof. Let x be an arbitrary element of X. Then since $X \subseteq Y$ we have, by definition, $x \in Y$. Similarly, from $Y \subseteq Z$ it follows that $x \in Z$. But x was an arbitrary element of X and hence $X \subseteq Z$.

THEOREM 2. If $X \subseteq Y$ and $X \subseteq Z$, then $X \subseteq YZ$.

Proof. Let x be an arbitrary element of X. Then from $X \subseteq Y$ it follows that $x \in Y$, and from $X \subseteq Z$, it follows that $x \in Z$. Together, these statements imply that $x \in YZ$ by the definition of intersection, and hence $X \subseteq YZ$.

THEOREM 3. If $X \subseteq Y$, then $X \subseteq Y + Z$ for any set Z.

Proof. Since $Y \subseteq Y + Z$ by the definition of union, this theorem follows at once from Theorem 1.

THEOREM 4. $X \subseteq Y$ if and only if $Y' \subseteq X'$.

Proof. First, assume that $X \subseteq Y$ and let y' be an arbitrary element in Y'. Then y' is not an element in Y, by definition of complement. But every element in X is an element in Y and hence y' is not an element in X. Hence y' must be an element in X'. Since y' represented any element of Y', it follows that $Y' \subseteq X'$.

Next, assume that $Y' \subseteq X'$. Then by the first part of this proof, $(X')' \subseteq (Y')'$ which reduces to $X \subseteq Y$, by the law of double complementation. This completes the proof of the theorem.

These theorems, which were easy to prove, have some rather interesting applications, one of which is to problems of a logical nature. Although we are not primarily interested in logic in this chapter, the algebra of logic and the algebra of sets are very closely related. For instance, one of the basic laws of logic is the law of *syllogism*, which is equivalent to Theorem 1. A classic example of the use of this law is the following.

EXAMPLE 1. Given that Socrates is a man, and that all men are mortal, it is required to show that Socrates is mortal. Although this type of argument is so familiar that any proof may seem absurd, the necessary steps in a formal proof using Theorem 1 are given to illustrate the general method.

Solution. Let the universal set be the set of all animate things; let X denote the set of all men, Y the set of all mortal things, and S the unit set consisting of Socrates alone. We are given that $S \subseteq X$ and $X \subseteq Y$. By Theorem 1 it follows that $S \subseteq Y$, which is the desired conclusion that Socrates is mortal.

The principle involved in the law of syllogism is familiar to everyone. Problems of similar type referring to Theorem 2, 3, or 4 are not quite so familiar. The following example and some of the problems in the exercises use several of these theorems in combination. These problems are artificial, but they illustrate the way in which the algebra of sets can help in interpreting complicated sets of statements. The use of symbolic notation makes trivial the forming of logical conclusions that would be difficult otherwise.

EXAMPLE 2. What conclusion can be drawn from the following statements?

(a) A man who is unhappy is not his own boss.
(b) All married men have responsibilities.
(c) Every man is either married, or is his own boss (or both).
(d) No man with responsibilities can fish every day.

Solution. Let the universal set be the set of all men, and denote other sets as follows:

H is the set of happy men,
B is the set of men who are their own bosses,
M is the set of married men,
R is the set of men with responsibilities,
F is the set of men who fish every day.

Statement (a) translates immediately into $H' \subseteq B'$, but by applying Theorem 4 we may also write the statement in symbols as follows:

(a) $B \subseteq H$.

Statement (b) tells us that $M \subseteq R$ or, equally well, by Theorem 4 we have

(b) $R' \subseteq M'$.

Statement (c) gives that $M + B = 1$, or referring to the equivalence of this statement with a condition of inclusion, we obtain

(c) $M' \subseteq B$.

Finally, from (d) we obtain the fact that $RF = 0$, which is equivalent to

(d) $F \subseteq R'$.

Combining (d) and (b) by Theorem 1 we obtain (e) $F \subseteq M'$. Again applying Theorem 1 to (e) and (c), we obtain (f) $F \subseteq B$. Finally, combining (f) and (a), we have (g) $F \subseteq H$. We will consider (g) as the major conclusion, which reads "All men who fish every day are happy." Note that each of (e) and (f) is also a conclusion that we obtained from the given statements.

Exercises

1. Write out proofs of Theorems 1 and 2, based on the fact that $X \subseteq Y$ is equivalent to $XY' = 0$.

2. Rewrite each of the following conditions on the sets X, Y, and Z, without the use of the symbol $\subseteq$:

(a) $X'Y \subseteq Z$ (b) $X + Y' \subseteq Z$
(c) $XY' + X'Y \subseteq Z + Y'$ (d) $X \subseteq Y' \subseteq Z$

3. Find an equivalent statement of set inclusion for each of the following conditions on sets X, Y, Z, and W:

(a) $(X' + Y)(Z + W')' = 0$ (b) $(X' + Y)(Z + W') = 0$
(c) $X + Y' + Z' + W' = 1$ (d) $XY' + Z'W = 0$

4. Given that for certain sets A, B, C, D, and E the following conditions hold: $A \subseteq C$, $B' \subseteq A'$, $CD' = 0$, show that $A \subseteq BD + E$.

5. Given that for certain sets A, B, C, D, and E the following conditions hold: $C' \subseteq A'$, $BC' = 0$, $C' + D = 1$, $CE = C$, show that $D' + E' \subseteq A'C'$.

6. Given that (a) All natives of Mindanao eat white people. (b) All natives of Borneo eat black people. (c) No man eats both black and white people. (d) Jones eats black people. Decide whether each of the following is a valid conclusion, and if it is, prove it by using the theorems in this section. Use for the universal set the set of all humans. Do not assume more than is given in (a), (b), (c), and (d).

(A) Jones is a native of Borneo.   (B) Jones is not a native of Mindanao.

7. What conclusion can be formed from the following statements?   (a) A student who does not study hard is not a good student.   (b) Good students

receive good grades. (c) A student who studies hard and receives good grades will secure a fine job.

8. What conclusion can be formed from the following statements? (a) A dishonorable man is never perfect. (b) An honorable man never lies. (c) A man is not perfect unless he is always tactful. (d) Every tactful man tells an occasional lie.

9. Given the following four statements concerning the student body at C.U.:

(1) All engineering students take mathematics.
(2) There are no women engineering students at C.U.
(3) Students who do not take mathematics are not chemists.
(4) Every student either is a woman or takes military science, or both.

Determine for each of the following statements whether or not it is derivable from the given statements. In each case where the statement *is* derivable, show the necessary steps in the derivation. Include a translation of each statement into symbols.

(a) Those students who do not take mathematics are not engineering students.
(b) No engineering students are chemists.
(c) All engineering students take both mathematics and military science.
(d) All engineering students are chemists.
(e) All those chemists who take education also take mathematics.
(f) Every woman engineering student is a chemist.

1–8 Conditional equations. By a *conditional equation* we mean a symbolic statement of the equality of two sets which, unlike the basic laws of Section 1–4, is not identically valid for arbitrary sets but is valid only for certain sets. Conditional equations arise in the stating of hypotheses and conclusions for theorems and in the statement of problems to be solved in the algebra of sets.

In considering two equations, we will say that the second is *derivable* from the first if the second can be obtained by applying any one or more of the following four rules to the first.

RULE 1. Any expression in either the left or right member of the equation may be replaced by any expression representing the identical set. That is, operations of simplifying, expanding, etc., may be performed independently on either member of the equation.

RULE 2. The right and left members of the equation may be simultaneously replaced by the respective complementary set.

RULE 3. Each side of the equation may be multiplied by the same set, or by equal sets.

RULE 4. The same set or equal sets may be added to each side of the equation.

These rules are valid in the sense that if the condition represented by the given equation holds for certain sets, then the condition represented by the derived equation will hold for these sets. The proof of this statement follows from the basic laws in the case of Rule 1, and from the fact that complementation, intersection, and union are uniquely defined, in the case of the other rules. As an example, each of the equations below is derivable from the preceding one, and hence from the first equation:

$Y + X = XZ$	assumed given
$(Y + X)' = (XZ)'$	by Rule 2
$X'Y' = X' + Z'$	by Rule 1, using (8a) and (8b)
$WX'Y' = W(X' + Z')$	by Rule 3
$WX'Y' = WX' + WZ'$	by Rule 1, using (3a)
$U + WX'Y' = U + WX' + WZ'$	by Rule 4

Two additional rules apply to sets of equations. The derivation of the rules is obvious.

RULE 5. An equation of the form $A + B = 0$ may be replaced by the two simultaneous equations $A = 0$ and $B = 0$, and conversely.

RULE 6. An equation of the form $AB = 1$ may be replaced by the two simultaneous equations $A = 1$ and $B = 1$, and conversely.

In considering two sets of simultaneous equations, we will say the second set is *derivable* from the first set if each equation of the second set is obtained from equations of the first set by the application of one or more of Rules 1 through 6.

In addition to specifying operations that may be performed upon equations, it is well to point out two which are *not* permissible. Neither of the cancellation laws for addition and multiplication is valid in the algebra of sets. That is, from $X + Y = X + Z$ it does not follow that $Y = Z$, and from $XY = XZ$ and $X \neq 0$ it does not follow that $Y = Z$. Since Rules 3 and 4 are not reversible, we need to consider another relationship between sets of equations which is stronger than the relation of derivability. We will say that two sets of equations are *equivalent* if each set is derivable from the other. Equivalent sets of equations represent identical restrictions on the sets involved in the equations.

The following theorem illustrates the importance of the role of conditional equations in the algebra of sets:

THEOREM. Any given collection of conditions imposed on sets which can be expressed in the notations of the algebra of sets is equivalent to a single equation with right member 0.

Proof. First, note that any condition expressible in algebraic notation must of necessity be either an equation expressing the equality of two sets or a statement of set inclusion. Since the condition $X \subseteq Y$ is equivalent to the equation $XY' = 0$, it suffices to consider only collections of equations.

Next we shall prove that every equation is equivalent to an equation with 0 as its right member. An arbitrary equation may be represented by the equation $A = B$. If both sides of this equation are multiplied by B', we obtain $AB' = 0$. Multiplying both sides by A', we obtain $A'B = 0$. Adding these equations gives the equation $AB' + A'B = 0$, an equation with 0 as its right member which is derivable from the given equation. Conversely, if we assume that $AB' + A'B = 0$, we may multiply both sides by B' to obtain $AB' = 0$. If the complement of both sides of $AB' + A'B = 0$ is taken, we obtain $AB + A'B' = 1$. Now, multiplying both sides by B, we have $AB = B$. Upon adding this to the equation $AB' = 0$, we obtain $AB + AB' = B$, or $A(B + B') = B$, or $A = B$. Hence the equation $A = B$ is derivable from $AB' + A'B = 0$, and with the first part of the proof this shows that the two equations are equivalent.

Finally, if each equation of the given collection is replaced by the appropriate equation of the form $X = 0$, these equations may be combined, by Rule 5, to form a single equation with 0 as its right member. This completes the proof.

In the course of the above proof a method was derived for converting an equation of the form $A = B$ into an equivalent equation of the form $C = 0$. Since this was not a part of the statement of the theorem, it is listed for easy reference in the following corollary.

COROLLARY. The equation $A = B$ is equivalent to the equation $AB' + A'B = 0$.

EXAMPLE 1. Replace the set of conditions (a) $X \subseteq Y$, (b) $X + Y = Z$, and (c) $Z + W = 1$ by a single equivalent condition of the form $A = 0$.

Solution.

$X \subseteq Y$ is equivalent to $XY' = 0$.
$X + Y = Z$ is equivalent to $(X + Y)Z' + (X + Y)'Z = 0$, by the corollary.
$Z + W = 1$ is equivalent to $Z'W' = 0$, by taking complements of both sides.

Adding these equations, we find that the required condition is $XY' + XZ' + YZ' + X'Y'Z + Z'W' = 0$. This condition might also be written in other forms.

EXAMPLE 2. Show that the following set of conditions is inconsistent:

(a) $A' \subseteq B$,   (b) $A = B$,   (c) $A' + B' = 1$.

Solution. To test a set of equations or conditions for consistency, we will replace the set by an equivalent equation with 0 on the right. If the equation reduces to $1 = 0$, the given set is clearly inconsistent. Otherwise, the equation simply represents a simplification of the given set of conditions. In this case we replace (a) by $A'B' = 0$, replace (b) by $AB' + A'B = 0$, and replace (c) by

$AB = 0$. Then, upon adding, we obtain $AB + AB' + A'B + A'B' = 0$. The left side reduces to 1 and hence the given conditions are equivalent to the equation $1 = 0$, which shows that the conditions were inconsistent.

EXERCISES

1. Show that the three equations $A = 1$, $X' + Y' = 1$, and $X + Y = 1$ are each derivable from the equation $A(X'Y + XY') = 1$.

2. Show that the set of conditions $X = Y$, $AX = BY$, $X \subseteq Z$ is equivalent to the single condition $X(Y' + AB' + Z') + Y(X' + A'B) = 0$.

3. Find the simplest condition, in the form of an equation with 0 as its right member, which is equivalent to the following set of conditions:

(a) $X + Y \subseteq X'Y$ (b) $A + X = B + X$ (c) $B + X' = 1$

4. Find and simplify a single condition in the form of an equation with 0 as its right member which is equivalent to the following set of conditions:

(a) $XY \subseteq Z$ (b) $X + Y = YZ$ (c) $XZ' = 0$ (d) $X \subseteq Z'Y$

5. Show that the following set of conditions is inconsistent:

(a) $Y + Z' \subseteq X$ (b) $X + W' = 1$ (c) $(X + Y'Z)(X + W') = 0$

6. The following set of rules governs the choice of committee members in a certain society. Simplify these rules; i.e., replace them by a simpler set expressing the same conditions.

(a) The members of the social committee shall be chosen from the membership of the executive council.

(b) No member of the executive council may serve on both the social committee and the financial committee.

(c) Any member of both the financial committee and the executive council shall automatically be placed on the social committee.

(d) No member of the publicity committee may serve on the social committee unless he is also a member of the executive council.

7. The mythical kingdom of Moo is closely guarded against intruders. As a result, the reports on conditions and customs in Moo are meager. Four adventurers returned from Moo with the following pieces of information:

First report: Everyone in Moo who wears a red feather is either married or owns a dog (or both).

Second report: There is no married person who does not wear a red feather unless the person is a witch.

Third report: All dog owners who wear red feathers are married.

Fourth report: There are no witches in Moo.

Assuming that all reports are true, determine exactly what facts are known about Moo. Write this information as simply as possible. (State your answer in reasonable English, not in symbols.)

8. A reporter at a certain costume party turned in a report containing the following four statements concerning the party guests. (The reporter himself is not counted as a guest.)

(1) All women at the party wore wigs.
(2) No man at the party wore a hat.
(3) Everyone at the party who wore a wig was a man and, furthermore, every man carried an umbrella but not a cane.
(4) Every man at the party who carried an umbrella either wore a hat or carried a cane or both.

As a result of this report, the reporter was fired. Explain why by showing that the report cannot be correct. Use Boolean algebra in your proof, state clearly the meaning of each symbol used, and show all steps clearly.

1–9 Solution of equations. In considering conditional equations, a natural question to ask is whether it is possible to solve an equation involving an unknown set, and if so, what types of solutions can be expected. We shall see that solution of equations is possible, but that in general the solution is not unique, but represents upper and lower bounds for the unknown set.

Suppose that an equation involving an unknown set X is given and that all letters other than X which appear in the equation represent known sets. This equation may be written in the form $p(X) = 0$, where $p(X)$ represents a polynomial. If $p(X)$ contains terms in which neither X nor X' appear, each such term may be multiplied by $X + X'$ to produce an equivalent equation of the form $AX + BX' = 0$. This equation is equivalent to the two equations $AX = 0$ and $BX' = 0$, or the condition that $B \subseteq X \subseteq A'$. Any set which satisfies this condition is a solution of the equation. B is termed the *least solution* and A' the *greatest solution* of the equation. Clearly, a solution exists if and only if $B \subseteq A'$ or, equivalently, if and only if $AB = 0$. This equation is called the *eliminant of X*, or the condition for consistency of the given equation.

Whether an equation is consistent or not will depend, in general, upon the meanings of the sets A and B. However, in some cases the condition $AB = 0$ may be satisfied (or cannot be satisfied) independently of the meanings of the sets. For example, the equation $CDX + C'X' = 0$ is consistent for arbitrary sets C and D, since $(CD)(C') = 0$ regardless of the meaning of C and D. Again, the equation $(M + M')X + X' = 0$ is inconsistent, regardless of the meaning of set M.

The solution of an equation is unique only in the case that $B = A'$, in the notation used above. Primarily because solutions are rarely unique, solving equations plays a very minor role in the algebra of sets. Artificial problems can be constructed, but they are of little practical importance.

EXAMPLE 1. Solve for X: $BX = C$.

Solution. This equation is equivalent to $BC'X + B'C + CX' = 0$, and if $B'C$ is multiplied by $X + X'$, we obtain $(B'C + BC')X + CX' = 0$. Hence the general solution is $C \subseteq X \subseteq (B'C' + BC)$. The eliminant is $(B'C + BC')C = 0$, or $B'C = 0$. That is, the equation is consistent provided $C \subseteq B$, and then any set between C and $B'C' + BC$ satisfies the equation.

Not only is it possible to solve a single equation for an unknown set X, but simultaneous equations or sets of conditions in any form can also be solved. Since we proved in Section 1–8 that any set of conditions is equivalent to a single equation, simultaneous equations always reduce to a single equation for which the method described above is adequate.

EXAMPLE 2. Determine the nature of set X if the following conditions are given: $AX' \subseteq B$, $B'X + C = 1$.

Solution. The two given conditions reduce to the single equation $AB'X' + BC' + C'X' = 0$. This equation is equivalent to $BC'X + (AB' + C')X' = 0$. Hence $(AB' + C') \subseteq X \subseteq (B' + C)$ is the general solution, and the condition for consistency is $BC' = 0$. If the conditions are consistent, any set X containing $AB' + C'$ will satisfy the conditions.

EXERCISES

Solve the following equations for X. In each case, find the general solution if there is one, and the eliminant of X.

1. $A + X = B$ 2. $C + DX = 0$ 3. $AX + BX = A'B'X$
4. $AB + ABX' + A'BX = 0$ 5. $AX + BX' = CX + DX'$
6. $B'X = 0$, $C'X = 0$, and $A' + B' + C' + X = 1$ (solve simultaneously).
7. $AX + BX' = AX + CX'$, and $DX + BX' = D'X + CX'$ (solve simultaneously).

1–10 The number of elements in a set. A number of applications of the algebra of sets, particularly in probability theory, depend upon the number of elements in a set. We will denote the number of elements in a set X by $n(X)$.

Suppose that for two sets A and B we know that $n(A) = 50$ and $n(B) = 100$. What can be said concerning $n(A + B)$ and $n(AB)$? It is apparent that if A and B have no elements in common, $n(A + B) = 150$ and $n(AB) = 0$. In the general case, we can say only that $100 \leq n(A + B) \leq 150$, where $n(A + B) = 100$ if and only if $A \subseteq B$. Likewise, $0 \leq n(AB) \leq 50$, where $n(AB) = 50$ only in the case $A \subseteq B$.

In general, if X and Y have no elements in common, we say that X and Y are *disjoint sets* and the formula $n(A + B) = n(A) + n(B)$ holds. In all cases the following theorem holds.

THEOREM 1. If X and Y are any two sets, then

$$n(X + Y) = n(X) + n(Y) - n(XY).$$

Proof. Since XY and XY' are disjoint sets and $X = XY + XY'$, it follows that $n(X) = n(XY) + n(XY')$. Similarly, $n(Y) = n(XY) + n(X'Y)$. Adding these two equations, we obtain $n(X) + n(Y) = n(XY') + n(X'Y) + 2n(XY)$, or $n(XY') + n(X'Y) = n(X) + n(Y) - 2n(XY)$. Next we note that XY', $X'Y$, and XY are disjoint sets, and

$$X + Y = X(Y + Y') + Y(X + X') = XY + XY' + XY + X'Y$$
$$= XY + XY' + X'Y.$$

Hence $n(X + Y) = n(XY) + n(XY') + n(X'Y)$ and, substituting from above, $n(X + Y) = n(X) + n(Y) - n(XY)$, which completes the proof.

COROLLARY.

$$n(X + Y + Z) = n(X) + n(Y) + n(Z) - n(XY) - n(XZ)$$
$$- n(YZ) + n(XYZ)$$

for any three sets X, Y, and Z.

The results of the theorem and corollary could be extended to include the case of four or more sets, but the resulting formulas become increasingly unwieldy. As an exercise, the student should attempt to write the general formula which holds for m sets. This formula is not often used, although the generalization of the method used in the first line of the proof of Theorem 1 is of considerable use in probability, as we shall see. This generalization is given in the following theorem:

THEOREM 2. If $Y_1, Y_2, \ldots, Y_m$ are arbitrary sets which are mutually disjoint and have the property that $Y_1 + Y_2 + \cdots + Y_m = 1$, then for any set X, $n(X) = n(XY_1) + n(XY_2) + \cdots + n(XY_m)$.

Proof. $X = X(1) = X(Y_1 + Y_2 + \cdots + Y_m) = XY_1 + XY_2 + \cdots + XY_m$, where the sets $XY_1, XY_2, \ldots, XY_m$ are mutually disjoint. From this the theorem follows.

EXAMPLE 1. (Taken from the Joint Associateship Examination for Actuaries, 1935, Part 5, question 9B.) Certain data obtained from a study of a group of 1000 employees in a cotton mill, as to their race, sex, and marital status, were unofficially reported as follows: 525 colored lives; 312 male lives; 470 married lives; 42 colored males; 147 married colored; 86 married males; 25 married colored males. Test this classification to determine whether the numbers reported in the various groups are consistent.

Solution. Let C be colored lives, M be male lives, W be married lives. Then

$$
\begin{aligned}
n(C + M + W) &= n(C) + n(M) + n(W) - n(CM) - n(MW) \\
&\qquad - n(CW) + n(CMW) \\
&= 525 + 312 + 470 - 42 - 86 - 147 + 25 \\
&= 1057.
\end{aligned}
$$

The conclusion is that the data are inconsistent, since the data referred to only 1000 employees.

Of course, in this example, it is possible that this check might have given a number less than 1000 even though the data were inconsistent. (See Problem 3 below.) In such a case, and in fact in any problem where the number of elements in two or more sets and their intersections are of interest, it is helpful to draw an appropriate Venn diagram and fill in the number of elements in each of the disjoint sets represented in the diagram.

EXAMPLE 2. The following information is given concerning the number of elements in the subsets A, B, C of a certain set with 200 elements: $n(A) = 70$, $n(B) = 120, n(C) = 90, n(AB) = 50, n(AC) = 30, n(BC) = 40$, and $n(ABC) = 20$. Find (a) $n(A + B)$, (b) $n(A + B + C)$, (c) $n(A'BC)$, and (d) $n(AB'C')$.

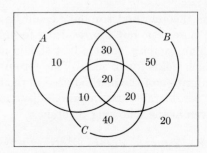

FIG. 1–3. Numbered Venn diagrams for Example 2.

Solution. The appropriate Venn diagram is given in Fig. 1–3. First, each of the regions in the diagram is labeled appropriately. Next, beginning with region ABC, the correct number of elements is filled in. Here the number is given as 20. Now the fact that $n(ABC') = 30$ is determined by subtracting $n(ABC)$ from $n(AB)$, since $n(AB) = n(ABC) + n(ABC')$. By continuing in this way, the number in each region is easily determined. If the data are inconsistent, the computed number of elements in some region will be negative, indicating that the given figures cannot be correct. If no inconsistency is present, any problem related to the diagram can be solved by inspection. The answers required in this example are: (a) 140, (b) 180, (c) 20, and (d) 10.

Exercises

1. Write out the proof of the Corollary to Theorem 1. (Apply the theorem to $n[X + (Y + Z)]$.)

2. Among the members of a certain fraternity, 70 take English, 40 take math, 40 take chemistry, 20 take math and English, 15 take math and chemistry, 25 take English and chemistry, and 5 take math, English, and chemistry. If all·fraternity members take at least one of the three, how many fraternity members are there?

3. Show that the following report is inconsistent. In a survey of 100 students concerning ability to read French, Spanish, and German, 46 read French, 25 read German, 27 read Spanish, 19 read French and German, 8 read French and Spanish, 10 read Spanish and German, and 3 read all three languages.

4. A certain number of red, white and blue tags are passed out among 100 people at a party. It is known that 45 people receive red tags, 45 people receive white tags, 60 people receive blue tags, 15 people receive both red and white tags, 25 people receive white and blue tags, 20 people receive red and blue tags, and 5 people receive all three colors.

(a) How many receive no tag? (b) How many receive exactly 1 tag? (c) How many receive exactly 2 tags? (d) How many receive a white tag but not a blue tag?

5. In a certain class there are 15 veterans, of which 10 are boys; 15 boys who are not veterans; and 30 girls. How many students are in the class?

6. (From Lewis Carroll.) In a very hotly fought battle, at least 70% of the combatants lost an eye, at least 75% lost an ear, at least 80% lost an arm, and at least 85% lost a leg. How many lost all four members? (Give the best answer possible in the form: "At least _____ percent lost all four.")

7. At a party for 100 children, a large basket of candy is suspended from the ceiling. Each piece of candy is wrapped in either red, white, or blue paper. At the end of the party, the basket is broken and the children scramble for the candy. The children are then asked about the types of candy they have, with the following results: 40 have a red one, 60 have a blue one, 70 have a white one, 20 have a red one and a blue one, 25 have a red one and a white one, and 30 have a blue one and a white one. The investigator forgot to ask if every child had at least one piece of candy. Show that exactly 5 had a piece of each color.

8. The following information concerns a group of 100 students: All men are more than 20 years old. There are 50 women in the group. There are 60 students over 20 years old. There are 25 married women. There are 15 married students over 20 years old. There are 10 married women over 20 years old.

Number a suitable Venn diagram as completely as possible and answer the following questions. (a) How many married students are there? (b) How many of the unmarried women are over 20? (c) How many of the unmarried men are under 20? (d) How many married men are there? (e) How many students are there under 20?

REFERENCES

ALLENDOERFER and OAKLEY, *Principles of Mathematics*, McGraw-Hill Book Co., Inc., 1955.

CULBERTSON, J. T., *Mathematics and Logic for Digital Devices*, D. Van Nostrand Co., 1958.

FREUND, JOHN E., *A Modern Introduction to Mathematics*, Prentice-Hall, Inc., 1956.

KEMENY, SNELL, and THOMPSON, *Introduction to Finite Mathematics*, Prentice-Hall, Inc., 1957.

MAY, K. O., *Elements of Modern Mathematics*, Addison-Wesley, 1959.

CHAPTER 2

BOOLEAN ALGEBRA

2–1 Introduction. An intuitive approach to the algebra of sets was followed in Chapter 1 in order to make the introduction to Boolean algebra as intuitive and natural as possible. All three of the applications of Boolean algebra mentioned in this book are readily treated in an elementary manner. However, to discuss each entirely separately, with separate proofs of all important theorems, is a needless waste of time. In addition, such a treatment would tend to emphasize the dissimilarities between the applications rather than their essential unity. For this reason, among others, the present chapter presents a treatment of Boolean algebras in general, based on a set of definitions and axioms from which all subsequent theorems are derived. There will be some duplication of the material introduced in Chapter 1, of course, but whereas the results of Chapter 1 were based on intuitive concepts and applied only to sets, results in this chapter are derived in a rigorous manner, and apply equally well in every Boolean algebra.

For many readers, this chapter may represent a first experience with the axiomatic treatment of algebra. As such, it should provide much more than a precise description of Boolean algebra. It will illustrate the methods used in the development and study of any mathematical system. In particular, it will help, by comparison, in understanding the algebra of numbers which, unfortunately, is often treated as a mass of more or less unrelated rules and examples rather than as an integrated logical system.

2–2 Preliminary definitions. Most of the sets dealt with in mathematics have an algebraic structure. That is, one or more rules of combination are defined between elements of the set. The most common examples of such sets are the various collections of numbers, such as the set of all integers, the set of all real numbers, and the set of all complex numbers. There are four rules of combination for the real numbers: addition, subtraction, multiplication and division. (The last rule is something of an exception, in that division by zero is not permitted.) In the algebra of sets we observed two rules of combination, intersection and union.

Before an axiomatic definition of Boolean algebra can be given, it is necessary to discuss the nature of such rules of combination, which we will term *binary operations*. The definition which follows uses a symbol "∘" to stand for an arbitrary binary operation. Specific examples of ∘ would be symbols such as $(+)$, $(\cdot)$, and $(-)$.

DEFINITION. A *binary operation* ∘ on a set M is a rule which assigns to each ordered pair (a, b) of elements of M a unique element $c = a \circ b$ in M.

EXAMPLE 1. The operation of subtraction is a binary operation on the set of all rational numbers (numbers of the form p/q, where p and q are integers and q is not zero) but is not a binary operation on the set of all positive integers. For any two rational numbers $A = p/q$ and $B = r/s$, the difference $A - B$ is uniquely defined and is another rational number $(ps - rq)/qs$, hence $(-)$ satisfies the conditions of the definition of a binary operation on the set of all rational numbers. However, the difference of two positive integers is not always a positive integer and hence $(-)$ does not represent a binary operation on the set of positive integers.

While addition, multiplication, subtraction, and division are familiar examples of binary operations, the definition does not restrict the concept even to the extent that it have any intuitive or useful meaning whatsoever. To dispel any illusions that the reader may have concerning this matter, we include the following example.

EXAMPLE 2. A set M consists of the three symbols ○, □, and △. Two binary operations (>) and (<) are defined on M by the following "multiplication" tables. To read the first table, for example, $a > b$ is found in the table in the row opposite a and in the column below b, where a and b may be any of the three symbols in M. Thus □ > △ = ○, and △ < ○ = ○.

>	○	□	△
○	○	△	□
□	△	□	○
△	□	○	△

<	○	□	△
○	○	□	△
□	○	□	△
△	○	□	△

Among the familiar binary operations, many satisfy certain simple identities, or laws, familiar from elementary algebra as well as from Chapter 1. The names of these laws are standard throughout mathematics, and not just in Boolean algebra.

DEFINITION. A binary operation ∘ on a set of elements M is *associative* if and only if for every a, b, and c in M,

$$a \circ (b \circ c) = (a \circ b) \circ c.$$

DEFINITION. A binary operation ∘ on a set M is *commutative* if and only if for every a and b in M,

$$a \circ b = b \circ a.$$

DEFINITION. If ∘ and ∗ are two binary operations on the same set M, ∘ is *distributive* over ∗ if and only if for every a, b, and c in M,

$$a \circ (b * c) = (a \circ b) * (a \circ c).$$

As examples, recall that in the algebra of classes, intersection and union were both commutative and associative, and each was distributive over the other. The distributive law for multiplication over addition is written as $a(b + c) = ab + ac$, and for addition over multiplication is written as $a + bc = (a + b)(a + c)$.

In considering the set of all integers under the operation of addition, the number 0 stands out as different from all others because of the property that $0 + a = a$ for every integer a. This property is extremely important, and algebraic systems which have such an element differ geratly from those which do not. The following definition gives a name to such elements.

DEFINITION. An element e in a class M is an *identity* for the binary operation ∘ if and only if $a \circ e = e \circ a = a$ for every element a in M.

In the set of all integers, 0 is an identity for the operation of addition and 1 is an identity for the operation of multiplication. The set of even integers has no identity for multiplication.

EXERCISES

1. Which of the following are binary operations on the set of all integers?

(a) addition   (b) multiplication   (c) subtraction   (d) division

2. Which of the following are binary operations on the set of all nonzero real numbers?

(a) addition   (b) multiplication   (c) subtraction   (d) division

3. Which binary operations in Exercises 1 and 2 are (a) commutative? (b) associative?

4. Referring to Example 2,

(a) Is > commutative? associative?
(b) Is < commutative? associative?
(c) Which, if either, of the operations > and < is distributive over the other?

5. What are the identity elements for (+) and (·) in the algebra of classes?

2–3 Definition and properties of a Boolean algebra.

The definition of a Boolean algebra which will be used here is the one given by Huntington in 1904. Many other sets of postulates could be chosen that would define the algebra equally well. This set has the property that no postulate can be derived from the remaining postulates.

DEFINITION. A class of elements B together with two binary operations $(+)$ and $(\cdot)$ (where $a \cdot b$ will be written ab) is a Boolean algebra if and only if the following postulates hold:

P_1. The operations $(+)$ and $(\cdot)$ are commutative.

P_2. There exist in B distinct identity elements 0 and 1 relative to the operations $(+)$ and $(\cdot)$, respectively.

P_3. Each operation is distributive over the other.

P_4. For every a in B there exists an element a' in B such that

$$a + a' = 1 \qquad \text{and} \qquad aa' = 0.$$

There is no reason why the two operations in the definition must be written $(+)$ and $(\cdot)$. Any two symbols would serve equally well. If a set with operations ∘ and ∗, or ∪ and ∩, satisfied the analogous postulates, it would be a Boolean algebra. $(+)$ and $(\cdot)$ were chosen only to conform with the notation used in the other chapters.

We notice immediately that the alegbra of sets satisfies all these postulates and hence is a Boolean algebra. We will prove that, conversely, every Boolean algebra satisfies all the basic laws listed in Section 1–5 for the algebra of sets. In fact, an even stronger statement can be made, to the effect that every Boolean algebra may be interpreted as an algebra of sets for some choice of universal set. However, there are many examples of Boolean algebras where the words "element" and "set" do not explicitly appear. A very important one is the Boolean algebra with just two elements 0 and 1 described in Problem 2 of the exercises at the end of this section, and in Chapters 3 and 4.

The remainder of this section will be devoted to proving that every Boolean algebra satisfies the basic laws of Chapter 1.

THEOREM 1. Every statement or algebraic identity deducible from the postulates of a Boolean algebra remains valid if the operations $(+)$ and $(\cdot)$, and the identity elements 0 and 1 are interchanged throughout. (This theorem is known as the *principle of duality*.)

Proof. The proof of this theorem follows at once from the symmetry of the postulates with respect to the two operations and the two identities.

If one statement or algebraic expression is obtained from another by a single application of the principle of duality, the second is said to be the *dual* of the first. In this case, it is clear that the first is also the dual of the second. Each of the following theorems contains two dual statements, with the exception of one in which the given proposition is its own dual. From Theorem 1, it is necessary to prove only one of each pair of dual statements. However, to illustrate the nature of duality, both proofs are given in Theorem 2.

It should be noted that the steps in one proof are dual statements to those in the other, and the justification for each step is the same postulate or theorem in one case as in the other.

THEOREM 2. For every element a in a Boolean algebra B,

$$a + a = a \quad \text{and} \quad aa = a.$$

Proof.

$$
\begin{aligned}
a &= a + 0 & \text{by } P_2 \\
&= a + aa' & \text{by } P_4 \\
&= (a + a)(a + a') & \text{by } P_3 \\
&= (a + a)(1) & \text{by } P_4 \\
&= a + a, & \text{by } P_2
\end{aligned}
$$

and similarly,

$$
\begin{aligned}
a &= a(1) & \text{by } P_2 \\
&= a(a + a') & \text{by } P_4 \\
&= aa + aa' & \text{by } P_3 \\
&= aa + 0 & \text{by } P_4 \\
&= aa. & \text{by } P_2
\end{aligned}
$$

THEOREM 3. For each element a in a Boolean algebra B,

$$a + 1 = 1 \quad \text{and} \quad a0 = 0.$$

Proof.

$$
\begin{aligned}
1 &= a + a' & \text{by } P_4 \\
&= a + a'(1) & \text{by } P_2 \\
&= (a + a')(a + 1) & \text{by } P_3 \\
&= 1(a + 1) & \text{by } P_4 \\
&= a + 1. & \text{by } P_2
\end{aligned}
$$

THEOREM 4. For each pair of elements a and b in a Boolean algebra B,

$$a + ab = a \quad \text{and} \quad a(a + b) = a.$$

Proof.

$$
\begin{aligned}
a &= 1a & \text{by } P_2 \\
&= (1 + b)a & \text{by Theorem 3} \\
&= 1a + ba & \text{by } P_3 \\
&= a + ba & \text{by } P_2 \\
&= a + ab. & \text{by } P_1
\end{aligned}
$$

THEOREM 5. In every Boolean algebra B, each of the binary operations $(+)$ and $(\cdot)$ is associative. That is, for every a, b, and c in B,

$$a + (b + c) = (a + b) + c \quad \text{and} \quad a(bc) = (ab)c.$$

Proof. First we will show that $a + a(bc) = a + (ab)c$, as follows:

$$
\begin{aligned}
a + a(bc) &= a & &\text{by Theorem 4} \\
&= a(a + c) & &\text{by Theorem 4} \\
&= (a + ab)(a + c) & &\text{by Theorem 4} \\
&= a + (ab)c. & &\text{by } P_3
\end{aligned}
$$

Next we will show that $a' + a(bc) = a' + (ab)c$, as follows:

$$
\begin{aligned}
a' + a(bc) &= (a' + a)(a' + bc) & &\text{by } P_3 \\
&= 1(a' + bc) & &\text{by } P_4 \\
&= a' + bc & &\text{by } P_2 \\
&= (a' + b)(a' + c) & &\text{by } P_3 \\
&= [1(a' + b)](a' + c) & &\text{by } P_2 \\
&= [(a' + a)(a' + b)](a' + c) & &\text{by } P_4 \\
&= (a' + ab)(a' + c) & &\text{by } P_3 \\
&= a' + (ab)c. & &\text{by } P_3
\end{aligned}
$$

Now if we multiply these two equations, we obtain

$$[a + a(bc)][a' + a(bc)] = [a + (ab)c][a' + (ab)c]. \qquad (2\text{–}1)$$

The left side of Eq. (2–1) may be reduced as follows:

$$
\begin{aligned}
[a + a(bc)][a' + a(bc)] &= [a(bc) + a][a(bc) + a'] & &\text{by } P_1 \\
&= a(bc) + aa' & &\text{by } P_3 \\
&= a(bc) + 0 & &\text{by } P_4 \\
&= a(bc). & &\text{by } P_2
\end{aligned}
$$

Similarly, the right side of (2–1) reduces as follows:

$$
\begin{aligned}
[a + (ab)c][a' + (ab)c] &= [(ab)c + a][(ab)c + a'] & &\text{by } P_1 \\
&= (ab)c + aa' & &\text{by } P_3 \\
&= (ab)c + 0 & &\text{by } P_4 \\
&= (ab)c. & &\text{by } P_2
\end{aligned}
$$

Hence Eq. (2–1), when simplified, reads

$$a(bc) = (ab)c,$$

and this statement is the associative law that we were to prove.

From now on, we shall write both $a(bc)$ and $(ab)c$ as abc, and similarly, we shall write both $(a + b) + c$ and $a + (b + c)$ as $a + b + c$.

THEOREM 6. The element a' associated with the element a in a Boolean algebra is unique. (That is, only one element a' satisfies the conditions of P_4.)

Proof. Suppose that $a + x = 1$, $ax = 0$, and also that $a + y = 1$, $ay = 0$. Then,

$$
\begin{aligned}
x &= 1x & &\text{by } P_2 \\
&= (a + y)x & &\text{by assumption} \\
&= (ax + yx) & &\text{by } P_3 \\
&= 0 + yx & &\text{by assumption} \\
&= yx & &\text{by } P_2 \\
&= xy & &\text{by } P_1 \\
&= xy + 0 & &\text{by } P_2 \\
&= xy + ay & &\text{by assumption} \\
&= (x + a)y & &\text{by } P_3 \\
&= 1y & &\text{by assumption} \\
&= y. & &\text{by } P_2
\end{aligned}
$$

Thus any two elements associated with a as specified in P_4 are equal. In other words, a' is uniquely determined by a. We will refer to a' as the complement of a, as we did in Chapter 1.

THEOREM 7. *For every a in a Boolean algebra B, $(a')' = a$.*

Proof. By P_4, $a + a' = 1$, and $aa' = 0$. But this is exactly the necessary condition that $(a')'$ is equal to a. By Theorem 6, no other element has this property.

THEOREM 8. *In any Boolean algebra, $0' = 1$ and $1' = 0$.*

Proof. By Theorem 3, $1 + 0 = 1$, and $(1)(0) = 0$. Since Theorem 6 shows that for each a there is only one element a', these equations imply that $0' = 1$, and $1' = 0$.

THEOREM 9. *For every a and b in a Boolean algebra B,*

$$(ab)' = a' + b' \qquad \text{and} \qquad (a + b)' = a'b'.$$

Proof. First,

$$
\begin{aligned}
(ab)(a' + b') &= aba' + abb' & &\text{by } P_3 \\
&= 0b + a0 = 0 + 0 = 0. & &\text{by } P_1, P_2, P_4, \text{Theorem 3}
\end{aligned}
$$

Further,

$$
\begin{aligned}
ab + a' + b' &= a' + b' + ab & &\text{by } P_1 \\
&= (a' + b' + a)(a' + b' + b) & &\text{by } P_3 \\
&= (1 + b')(1 + a') & &\text{by } P_4 \text{ and } P_1 \\
&= 1. & &\text{by Theorem 3 and } P_2
\end{aligned}
$$

Now from P_4 and Theorem 6 these conditions imply that $(ab)' = a' + b'$. The dual follows from Theorem 1.

This completes the proofs of all properties given in the fundamental laws in Section 1–5. Hence all theorems proved in Chapter 1 from these laws hold in every Boolean algebra. In particular, any methods of simplification we have learned apply in general. To carry over the results derived on conditional equations, it is necessary to introduce the relation $\subseteq$ in a general Boolean algebra. This is done by the following definition.

DEFINITION. The "order" relation $a \subseteq b$ is defined by the statement: For every a and b in a Boolean algebra B, $a \subseteq b$ if and only if $ab' = 0$.

The following theorem contains the contents of four theorems in Section 1–7 which were derived there intuitively for sets. The proof here is based on the definition of the relation.

THEOREM 10. The following four properties of $\subseteq$ are valid in every Boolean algebra for arbitrary elements x, y, and z:

(a) If $x \subseteq y$ and $y \subseteq z$, then $x \subseteq z$.
(b) If $x \subseteq y$ and $x \subseteq z$, then $x \subseteq yz$.
(c) If $x \subseteq y$, then $x \subseteq y + z$ for any z.
(d) $x \subseteq y$ if and only if $y' \subseteq x'$.

Proof. The reasons for the steps in the proofs have been omitted, but should be supplied by the reader.

(a) $x \subseteq y$ is equivalent to $xy' = 0$ and $y \subseteq z$ is equivalent to $yz' = 0$. Hence $xz' = xz'(y + y') = xyz' + xy'z' = 0 + 0 = 0$. But $xz' = 0$ is equivalent to $x \subseteq z$, which was to be shown.

(b) From $x \subseteq y$ and $x \subseteq z$ we have $xy' = 0$ and $xz' = 0$. Hence $xy' + xz' = 0$ and $x(y' + z') = 0$. But by Theorem 9, $y' + z' = (yz)'$ and thus $x(yz)' = 0$ or, equivalently, $x \subseteq yz$.

(c) From $x \subseteq y$ we have $xy' = 0$ and hence $x(y + z)' = x(y'z') = (xy')z' = 0$. But $x(y + z)' = 0$ is equivalent to $x \subseteq y + z$ and (c) is proven.

(d) Assume first that $x \subseteq y$ and thus $xy' = 0$. Then $0 = xy' = (x')'y' = y'(x')'$, and from this we have that $y' \subseteq x'$. Conversely, if $y' \subseteq x'$, then, applying the preceding statement, $(x')' \subseteq (y')'$ and by Theorem 7 this gives $x \subseteq y$.

EXERCISES

1. Write out the proof that $a0 = 0$ in Theorem 3, referring each step to the correct postulate.

2. Show that the class B consisting of 0 and 1 alone, together with the operations defined by the following tables, is a Boolean algebra.

+	0	1
0	0	1
1	1	1

·	0	1
0	0	0
1	0	1

3. Prove that in every Boolean algebra $a + a'b = a + b$ for every pair of elements a and b.

4. Prove that if $a + x = b + x$, and $a + x' = b + x'$, then $a = b$. [*Hint:* Compare with the proof of Theorem 5.]

5. Prove that if $ax = bx$ and $ax' = bx'$, then $a = b$.

6. Prove that for any a, b, and c in a Boolean algebra, the following four expressions are equal:

(a) $(a + b)(a' + c)(b + c)$ (b) $ac + a'b + bc$
(c) $(a + b)(a' + c)$ (d) $ac + a'b$.

7. Show that the set $\{a, b, c, d\}$ with operations $(+)$ and $(\cdot)$, defined below, is a Boolean algebra.

$+$	a	b	c	d
a	a	b	c	d
b	b	b	b	b
c	c	b	c	b
d	d	b	b	d

$\cdot$	a	b	c	d
a	a	a	a	a
b	a	b	c	d
c	a	c	c	a
d	a	d	a	d

8. Prove that in a Boolean algebra every triple of elements a, b, c satisfies the identity $ab + bc + ca = (a + b)(b + c)(c + a)$.

9. Prove that if a and b are elements of a Boolean algebra B satisfying the relation $a \subseteq b$, then $a + bc = b(a + c)$ for every element c in B. (This property is known as the *modular law*.)

10. Prove that if a, b, and c are elements in a Boolean algebra B for which *both* the conditions $ab = ac$ and $a + b = a + c$ hold, then it follows that $b = c$.

11. Prove that no Boolean algebra can have exactly three distinct elements.

2–4 Disjunctive normal form.

The words "monomial," "polynomial," "term," and "factor" used in Chapter 1 will now be used in connection with an arbitrary Boolean algebra. In addition, we shall use the word *constant* for any single symbol which represents a specified element of a Boolean algebra. 0 and 1 are examples of constants. The word *variable* will refer to any literal symbol x, y, etc., used to represent an arbitrary or unspecified element of a Boolean algebra. By a *Boolean function* we will mean any expression which represents the combination of a finite set of symbols, each representing a constant or a variable, by the operations of $(+)$, $(\cdot)$, or $(')$. Thus $(a' + b)'c + ab'x + 0$ is a Boolean function provided that each of the symbols a, b, c, x represents an element of a Boolean algebra. Similarly, each algebraic expression of Chapter 1 referring to a set is a Boolean function. For example, the equation $x + x' = 1$ represents the statement that a function $x + x'$ of the variable x equals the constant 1.

Among the functions of n variables $x_1, x_2, \ldots, x_n$ which can be written, a particular class of functions is of special interest, namely, those written as a sum of terms in which each term is a product involving all n variables either with or without a prime. Examples of such functions are $x + x'$, xy', $xyz' + x'yz + xy'z$ in one, two, and three variables, respectively. The following definition gives a name to such functions.

DEFINITION. A Boolean function is said to be in *disjunctive normal form in n variables* $x_1, x_2, \ldots, x_n$, for $n > 0$, if the function is a sum of terms of the type $f_1(x_1)f_2(x_2) \cdots f_n(x_n)$, where $f_i(x_i)$ is x_i or x_i' for each $i = 1, 2, \ldots, n$, and no two terms are identical. In addition, 0 and 1 are said to be in disjunctive normal form in n variables for any $n \geq 0$.

Some important properties of the disjunctive normal form are given in the following theorems.

THEOREM 1. Every function in a Boolean algebra which contains no constants is equal to a function in disjunctive normal form.

Proof. Let an arbitrary function (without constants) of the n variables $x_1, x_2, \ldots, x_n$ be denoted by f. If f contains an expression of the form $(A + B)'$ or $(AB)'$ for some functions A and B, Theorem 9 of Section 2–3 may be applied to yield $A'B'$ and $A' + B'$, respectively. This process may be continued until each prime which appears applies only to a single variable x_i.

Next, by applying the distributive law of $(\cdot)$ over $(+)$, f can be reduced to a polynomial.

Now suppose some term t does not contain either x_i or x_i' for some variable x_i. This term may be multiplied by $x_i + x_i'$ without changing the function. Continuing this process for each missing variable in each of the terms in f will give an equivalent function whose terms contain x_j or x_j' for each $j = 1, 2, \ldots, n$.

Finally, Theorem 2 of Section 2–3 allows the elimination of duplicate terms, and with this the proof is complete.

EXAMPLE 1. Write the function $f = (xy' + xz)' + x'$ in disjunctive normal form.

Solution.
$$
\begin{aligned}
(xy' + xz)' + x' &= (xy')'(xz)' + x' \\
&= (x' + y)(x' + z') + x' \\
&= x' + x'y + yz' + x' \\
&= x'(y + y')(z + z') + yz'(x + x') \\
&= x'yz + x'yz' + x'y'z + x'y'z' + xyz' + x'yz' \\
&= x'yz + xyz' + x'yz' + x'y'z + x'y'z'.
\end{aligned}
$$

The usefulness of the normal form lies primarily in the fact that each function uniquely determines a normal form in a given number of variables, as we shall see in later theorems. However, any function may be placed in normal form in more than one way by changing the number of variables.

For example, $f = xy$ is in normal form in x and y, but if xy is multiplied by $z + z'$, then $f = xyz + xyz'$ is also in normal form in the variables x, y, and z. Similarly, $g = x'yz + xyz + x'yz' + xyz'$ is in normal form in x, y, and z, but reduces, on factoring, to $g = x'y + xy$, which is in normal form in x and y. From now on we shall assume that unless stated otherwise, disjunctive normal form refers to that disjunctive normal form which contains the smallest possible number of variables. With this exception, we will be able to show that the normal form of a function is uniquely determined by the function.

Suppose that we desire to select a single term out of the possible terms in a disjunctive normal form in n variables. This corresponds to selecting either x_i or x_i' for each of the n variables x_i, $i = 1, 2, \ldots, n$. Thus there are exactly 2^n distinct terms which may occur in a normal form in n variables.

DEFINITION. That disjunctive normal form in n variables which contains 2^n terms is called the *complete disjunctive normal form* in n variables.

It will be a consequence of the following theorems that the complete disjunctive normal form is identically 1. A simple argument to prove this directly is to note that for any variable x_j, the coefficients of x_j and x_j' must be identical in a complete normal form, namely, these coefficients are each the complete normal form in the remaining $n - 1$ variables. Factoring serves to eliminate x_j, and this process may be repeated to eliminate each variable in succession, thus reducing the expression to 1.

THEOREM 2. If each of n variables is assigned the value 0 or 1 in an arbitrary, but fixed, manner, then exactly one term of the complete disjunctive normal form in the n variables will have the value 1 and all other terms will have the value 0.

Proof. Let $a_1, a_2, \ldots, a_n$ represent the values assigned to $x_1, x_2, \ldots, x_n$ in that order, where each a_i is 0 or 1. Select a term from the complete normal form as follows: use x_i if $a_i = 1$, and use x_i' if $a_i = 0$ for each x_i, $i = 1, 2, \ldots, n$. The term so selected is then a product of n ones, and hence is 1. All other terms in the complete normal form will contain at least one factor 0 and hence will be 0.

COROLLARY. Two functions are equal if and only if their respective disjunctive normal forms contain the same terms.

Proof. Two functions with the same terms are obviously equal. Conversely, if two functions are equal, then they must have the same value for every choice of value for each variable. In particular, they assume the same value for each set of values 0 and 1 which may be assigned to the variables. By Theorem 2, the combinations of values of 0 and 1 which, when assigned to the variables, make the function assume the value 1 uniquely determine the terms which are present in the normal form for the function. Hence both normal forms contain the same terms.

COROLLARY. To establish any identity in Boolean algebra, it is sufficient to check the value of each function for all combinations of 0 and 1 which may be assigned to the variables.

We have seen in the preceding theorems that a function is completely determined by the values it assumes for each possible assignment of 0 and 1 to the respective variables. This suggests that functions could be conveniently specified by giving a table to represent such properties. In applications, particularly to the design of circuits, this is precisely the way in which Boolean functions are constructed. If such a table has been given, then the function, in disjunctive normal form, may be written down by inspection. For each set of conditions for which the function is to be 1, a corresponding term is included in the disjunctive normal form selected, as indicated in the proof of Theorem 2. The sum of these terms gives the function, although not necessarily in simplest form. The following example indicates this method. Some short cuts for simplification will be pointed out in Chapter 5, but for the present any simplifying will be performed in the usual way after the function is obtained in disjunctive normal form.

EXAMPLE 2. Find and simplify the function $f(x, y, z)$ specified by Table 2–1. (Note that the table shows the value of f for each of the $2^3 = 8$ possible assignments of 0 and 1 to x, y, and z.)

Solution. We observe that for the combinations represented by rows 2, 3, and 7 of the table the function will have the value 1. Thus the disjunctive normal form of f will contain three terms. Selecting these terms as described in the proof of Theorem 2, we obtain $f(x, y, z) = xyz' + xy'z + x'y'z = xyz' + y'z$. Checking this function for each combination listed in the table verifies that f has the required properties.

TABLE 2–1

VALUES OF $f(x, y, z)$ FOR EXAMPLE 2

Row	x	y	z	$f(x, y, z)$
1	1	1	1	0
2	1	1	0	1
3	1	0	1	1
4	1	0	0	0
5	0	1	1	0
6	0	1	0	0
7	0	0	1	1
8	0	0	0	0

A simple application of the results of this section is in finding, by inspection, the complement of any function in disjunctive normal form. The complement will contain exactly those terms of the complete normal form missing from the given function. As examples, the complement of $a'b + ab'$ is $ab + a'b'$, and the complement of $abc + ab'c + ab'c' + a'b'c'$ is $a'bc + abc' + a'b'c + a'bc'$.

EXERCISES

1. Express each of the following in disjunctive normal form in the smallest possible number of variables:

(a) $x + x'y$

(b) $xy' + xz + xy$

(c) $(u + v + w)(uv + u'w)'$

(d) $xyz + (x + y)(x + z)$

(e) $(x'y + xyz' + xy'z + x'y'z't + t')'$

(f) $(x + y')(y + z')(z + x')(x' + y')$

(g) $(x + y)(x + y')(x' + z)$

(h) $x'yz + xy'z' + x'y'z + x'yz' + xy'z + x'y'z'$

2. Write out the terms of the complete disjunctive normal form in x, y, and z. Determine which term equals 1 if

(a) $x = 1$ and $y = z = 0$

(b) $x = z = 1$ and $y = 0$

3. Write each of the following in disjunctive normal form in the three variables x, y, and z:

(a) $x + y'$ (b) $x'z + xz'$ (c) $(x + y)(x' + y')$ (d) x

4. Write out all 16 possible functions of two variables x and y.

5. Write the function of three variables x, y, and z which is 1 if either $x = y = 1$ and $z = 0$, or if $x = z = 1$ and $y = 0$; and is 0 otherwise.

6. Write the function of x, y, and z which is 1 if and only if any two or more of the variables are 1.

7. Write separately, and simplify, the three functions f_1, f_2, and f_3 specified by Table 2–2.

TABLE 2–2

Row	x	y	z	f_1	f_2	f_3
1	1	1	1	0	0	1
2	1	1	0	1	1	1
3	1	0	1	0	1	0
4	1	0	0	1	0	0
5	0	1	1	0	0	0
6	0	1	0	0	1	0
7	0	0	1	0	1	1
8	0	0	0	0	0	1

8. Reduce the complete disjunctive normal form in the three variables x, y, and z to 1 by successive elimination of the variables.

9. Find, by inspection, the complement of each of the following:

(a) $xy + x'y$　　　　　　　　　　　　(b) xyz

(c) $uvw + u'v'w + uv'w' + u'vw'$　　　(d) $x'y'z' + x'yz + xy'z'$

10. Prove that there are exactly 2^{2^n} distinct functions of n variables in a Boolean algebra.

2–5 Conjunctive normal form. There are other normal forms, besides the disjunctive normal form, which are equally useful. One of these represents each function as a product of sums, rather than as a sum of products. If each statement in the preceding section were replaced by its dual, the resulting discussion would be a corresponding treatment of this second form called the *conjunctive* normal form. To make this clear, the definition and theorems are repeated here in their dual forms. No proofs are needed, of course, because of the principle of duality.

DEFINITION. A Boolean function is said to be in *conjunctive normal form in n variables* x_1, x_2, ..., x_n, for $n > 0$, if the function is a product of factors of the type $f_1(x_1) + f_2(x_2) + \cdots + f_n(x_n)$, where $f_i(x_i)$ is x_i or x_i' for each $i = 1, 2, \ldots, n$, and no two factors are identical. In addition, 0 and 1 are said to be in conjunctive normal form in n variables for $n \geq 0$.

THEOREM 1. Every function in a Boolean algebra which contains no constants is equal to a function in conjunctive normal form.

EXAMPLE 1. Write the function $(xy' + xz)' + x'$ in conjunctive normal form.

Solution. The procedure is essentially dual to that of Example 1, Section 2–4, although, depending on the initial form of the function, it may require more steps to perform the reduction in one case than in another. Here, after primes are removed from parentheses, the function is factored into linear factors and then extra variables are introduced as needed by adding, within each factor, products of the form ww'. The final step is to expand into linear factors again and remove like factors. The solution for this example is given by the steps below.

$$
\begin{aligned}
(xy' + xz)' + x' &= (x' + y)(x' + z') + x' \\
&= (x' + x' + y)(x' + x' + z') \\
&= (x' + y)(x' + z') \\
&= (x' + y + zz')(x' + z' + yy') \\
&= (x' + y + z)(x' + y + z')(x' + z' + y)(x' + y' + z') \\
&= (x' + y + z)(x' + y + z')(x' + y' + z').
\end{aligned}
$$

DEFINITION. That conjunctive normal form in n variables which contains 2^n factors is called the *complete conjunctive normal form* in n variables.

THEOREM 2. If each of n variables is assigned the value 0 or 1 in an arbitrary, but fixed, manner, then exactly one factor of the complete conjunctive normal form in the n variables will have the value 0 and all other factors will have the value 1.

Note that to select the factor which will be 0 when a set of values a_1, $a_2, \ldots, a_n$ are assigned to $x_1, x_2, \ldots, x_n$ in that order, where each a_i is 0 or 1, we simply dualize the method of Section 2–4: x_i is selected if $a_i = 0$, and x_i' is selected if $a_i = 1$ for each $i = 1, 2, \ldots, n$. The proper factor is then the sum of these letters, each of which has value 0. All other factors have the value 1.

COROLLARY. Two functions, each expressed in conjunctive normal form in n variables, are equal if and only if they contain identical factors.

EXAMPLE 2. Find and simplify the function $f(x, y, z)$ specified in Table 2–3.

TABLE 2–3

Row	x	y	z	$f(x, y, z)$
1	1	1	1	1
2	1	1	0	1
3	1	0	1	0
4	1	0	0	1
5	0	1	1	1
6	0	1	0	1
7	0	0	1	0
8	0	0	0	1

Solution. Since only two rows of the table show the value 0 for the function, it is easiest to use the dual of the method of Example 2, Section 2–4, and write the function first in conjunctive normal form. Selecting factors so that the function will be 0 for the conditions of rows 3 and 7, we have

$$f(x, y, z) = (x' + y + z')(x + y + z') = y + z'.$$

In problems of this type, the disjunctive normal form would normally be used if the number of 1's were less than the number of 0's in the f column, and the conjunctive normal form would be used if the number of 0's were less than the number of 1's.

Again, as in Section 2–4, we can use the conjunctive normal form to find complements of functions written in this form by inspection. The complement of any function written in conjunctive normal form is that function whose factors are exactly those factors of the complete conjunctive normal form which are missing from the given function. For example, the complement of $(x + y')(x' + y)$ is $(x + y)(x' + y')$.

It may be desirable to change a function from one normal form to the other. This can be done more readily than by following the general procedure for converting a function to a particular form. An example will illustrate the method, which is based on the fact that $(f')' = f$.

EXAMPLE 3. Find the conjunctive normal form for the function

$$f = xyz + x'yz + xy'z' + x'yz'.$$

Solution. $f = xyz + x'yz + xy'z' + x'yz'$
$= [(xyz + x'yz + xy'z' + x'yz')']'$
$= [(x' + y' + z')(x + y' + z')(x' + y + z)(x + y' + z)]'$
$= (x + y + z)(x' + y + z')(x + y + z')(x' + y' + z).$

Here the first complement was taken with the aid of DeMorgan's law and the second complement was taken by the method discussed above. These steps could have been reversed, with the same results. A similar procedure will change a function from conjunctive normal form to disjunctive normal form.

EXERCISES

1. Express each of the following in conjunctive normal form in the smallest possible number of variables:

(a) $x + x'y$ (b) $xy' + xz + xy$
(c) $(u + v + w)(uv + u'w)'$ (d) $xyz + (x + y)(x + z)$
(e) $(x'y + xyz' + xy'z + x'y'z't + t')'$
(f) $(x + y')(y + z')(z + x')(x' + y')$
(g) $(x + y)(x + y')(x' + z)$
(h) $x'yz + xy'z' + x'y'z + x'yz' + xy'z + x'y'z'$

2. Write out the factors of the complete conjunctive normal form in x, y, and z. Determine which factor equals 0 if

(a) $x = 1$ and $z = y = 0$ (b) $x = z = 1$ and $y = 0$

3. Write each of the following in conjunctive normal form in the three variables x, y, and z:

(a) $x + y'$ (b) $x'z + xz'$
(c) $(x + y)(x' + y')$ (d) x

4. Write the function of x, y, and z that is 0 if and only if any two or more of the variables are 0.

5. Find, by inspection, the complement of each of the following:

(a) $(x + y)(x' + y)(x' + y')$ (b) $(x + y + z)(x' + y' + z')$
(c) $(x' + y + z)(x + y' + z)(x + y + z')(x' + y' + z')$

6. Change each of the following from disjunctive normal form to conjunctive normal form:

(a) $uv + u'v + u'v'$

(b) $abc + ab'c' + a'bc' + a'b'c + a'b'c'$

7. Change each of the following from conjunctive normal form to disjunctive normal form:

(a) $(x + y')(x' + y)(x' + y')$

(b) $(u + v + w)(u + v + w')(u + v' + w)(u' + v + w')(u' + v' + w)$
$\times (u' + v' + w')$

8. Write separately, and simplify, the four functions f_1, f_2, f_3, and f_4 given by Table 2–4. Use whichever normal form seems easier.

TABLE 2–4

Row	x	y	z	f_1	f_2	f_3	f_4
1	1	1	1	1	0	0	1
2	1	1	0	0	1	1	1
3	1	0	1	1	0	0	1
4	1	0	0	1	0	1	0
5	0	1	1	1	0	1	1
6	0	1	0	1	0	1	1
7	0	0	1	0	1	0	1
8	0	0	0	1	0	0	0

2–6 Representation of a Boolean algebra. It may seem strange to the reader that, except for the difference in presentation as an axiomatic system, an arbitrary Boolean algebra has so much in common with an algebra of sets. The theorems in Chapter 2 are merely duplications of ideas already developed in Chapter 1. We have shown that every algebra of sets is a Boolean algebra. It is natural to conjecture whether an arbitrary Boolean algebra can be interpreted as an algebra of sets associated with some specially chosen universal set. That this is the case has been shown by M. H. Stone in a paper entitled "The Theory of Representations for Boolean Algebras," *Transactions of the American Mathematical Society*, Vol. 40, pp. 37–111. A proof of the representation theorem is beyond the scope of this text, but a discussion of the meaning of the theorem may be of interest.

In discussing algebraic systems, each consisting of a set of elements, and one or more operations which satisfy a given set of axioms, we say that two systems are *isomorphic* if the following relationship exists. First, it is necessary that for each operation in one system there is a corresponding operation in the second, although it may have a different name or symbol. The second requirement is that the elements of the two systems can be paired in such a way that each element of one system is paired with exactly one element of the second system, and conversely. If both sets are finite, this requirement implies that each set have the same number of elements. The third requirement is that this pairing can be arranged so that if a "multiplication" table for any operation were constructed for one system and if each symbol x in the table were replaced by the symbol from the other system which is paired with that particular x, then the resulting table would be the correct table for the corresponding operation in the second system. In brief, the two systems are required to be identical except for the names and symbols used to describe the elements and operations. The representation theorem can now be stated more explicitly.

THEOREM. Every abstract Boolean algebra is isomorphic to an algebra of sets.

This means that any thorough discussion of algebras of sets is automatically general enough to be considered as a discussion of arbitrary Boolean algebras. This gives another reason for the order of presentation of material in this text. While it may have appeared that we were limiting the discussion in Chapter 1 to a special case, this discussion was actually general, except for the words such as "set" and "element" which aided our intuition.

The importance of theorems like this can hardly be overstated. One of the most obvious values is that in replacing an abstract system with an equivalent and highly intuitive system, new ideas and theorems may be suggested that would have remained undiscovered otherwise. The usefulness of this process is not too dissimilar from the value of a graph as an aid to understanding the properties of an algebraic function.

In the following chapter on symbolic logic, we will see that it is often helpful to think of logical problems as problems in an algebra of sets. That this is possible is due to the representation theorem.

REFERENCES

ANDREE, R. V., *Selections from Modern Abstract Algebra*, Holt, 1958.

BIRKHOFF and MACLANE, *A Survey of Modern Algebra*, MacMillan, 1948.

HUNTINGTON, E. V., Postulates for the Algebra of Logic, *Trans. Am. Math. Soc.* 5 (1904).

JOHNSON, R. E., *First Course in Abstract Algebra*, Prentice-Hall, 1953.

STABLER, E. R., *An Introduction to Mathematical Thought*, Addison-Wesley, 1953.

STONE, M. H., The Theory of Representations for Boolean Algebras, *Trans. Am. Math. Soc.* 40, 37–111 (1936).

CHAPTER 3

SYMBOLIC LOGIC AND THE ALGEBRA OF PROPOSITIONS

3-1 Introduction. The purpose of this chapter is not to present a complete account of symbolic logic, but rather to introduce the subject in a way which will prepare the student for the task of reading a more comprehensive work. In addition to laying a background for further study, this chapter will present enough of the basic ideas of symbolic logic to give an appreciation of the role the subject plays in mathematics, and to illustrate that the algebra of logic is another example of a Boolean algebra.

Logic is an extensive field of study with many special areas of inquiry. In general, logic is concerned with the study and analysis of methods of reasoning or argumentation. Symbolic logic is not precisely defined as distinct from logic in general, but might be described as a study of logic which employs an extensive use of symbols.

In any discussion of logic, the treatment centers around the concept of a proposition (statement). The principal tool for treatment of propositions is the algebra of propositions, a Boolean algebra. In talking about propositions, we will also investigate certain logical forms which represent acceptable techniques for constructing precise proofs of theorems. Since statements are formed from words, it is apparent that some consideration must be given to words and their meanings. No logical argument can be based on words that are not precisely described. That part of logic which is concerned with the structure of statements is much more difficult than the areas mentioned previously, and in fact, has not been satisfactorily formalized. We will limit our attention to a few types of sentence construction that are of special interest in the formulation of mathematical statements.

3-2 Propositions and definitions of symbols. In the algebra of sets we found that it was necessary to start with certain primitive concepts in the form of undefined terms. This is typical of any formal system and is true of the algebra of propositions as well. The terms *true*, *false*, and *proposition* will be taken here as undefined. Without any attempt to investigate the philosophical meaning of truth and falsehood, we will assume that the words *true* and *false* are attributes which apply to propositions. By a *proposition*, we will infer the content of meaning of any declarative sentence which is free of ambiguity and which has the property that it is either true or false, but not both.

The discussion in the preceding paragraph helps our intuition in selecting suitable applications for the concept of a proposition, but it is not a definition. It may not even be apparent that propositions exist, since to be completely free of ambiguity is a requirement that would be difficult to justify for any given statement. The requirement is no more idealistic than the requirement in geometry that a line have no width. Certainly no such line can be drawn with a pencil or can even be proved to exist in the physical world. We will be somewhat tolerant, then, in our selection of statements which are suitable to be called propositions. The following examples are typical propositions:

> 3 is a prime number;
> when 5 is added to 4, the sum is 7;
> living creatures exist on the planet Venus.

Note that of these propositions, the first is known to be true, the second is known to be false, and the third is either true or false (not both), although our knowledge is not sufficient to decide at present which is the case. Contrast this with the following sentence, which is *not* a proposition:

> this statement you are reading is false.

If we assume that the statement is true, then from its content we infer that it is false. On the other hand, if the statement is assumed to be false, then from its content we infer that it is true. Therefore this statement fails to satisfy our requirements and is not a proposition.

We shall use lower case italic letters p, q, r, ... to represent propositions. Where no specific proposition is given, these will be called *propositional variables* and used to represent arbitrary propositions.

From any proposition, or set of propositions, other propositions may be formed. The simplest example is that of forming from the proposition p the *negation* of p, denoted by p'. For any proposition p, we define p' to be the proposition "it is false that p." For example, suppose that p is the proposition

> sleeping is pleasant.

The negation of this proposition would be the proposition

> it is false that sleeping is pleasant.

Since this statement is somewhat awkward, it is convenient to reword it to conform more closely with common usage. Other wordings that are equally acceptable are the following:

> sleeping is not pleasant;
> sleeping is unpleasant.

Regardless of the wording, it is essential that the negation be worded in such a way that it has the opposite truth value to that of the original proposition. When p is true, p' is false and when p is false, p' is true.

Any two propositions p and q may be combined in various ways to form new propositions. To illustrate, let p be the proposition

ice is cold,

and let q be the proposition

blood is green.

These propositions may be combined by the connective *and* to form the proposition

ice is cold and blood is green.

This proposition is referred to as the *conjunction* of p and q. In general, we define the *conjunction of p and q* for arbitrary propositions p and q to be the proposition "both p and q." In wording this proposition, the word *both* is often omitted. We will denote the conjunction of p and q by pq, and we will require that the proposition be true in those cases in which both p and q are true, and false in cases in which either one or both of p and q are false.

Another way in which the propositions in the preceding paragraph may be combined is indicated in the proposition

either ice is cold or blood is green.

This proposition is referred to as the *disjunction* of p and q. The use of "either . . . or . . ." in English is ambiguous in that some usages imply "either . . . or . . . or both," but other usages imply "either . . . or . . . , but not both." Consider, for example:

this creature is either a dog or an animal;
the baby is either a boy or a girl.

The first of these is called *inclusive* disjunction, and allows the possibility that both may be the case. This is the sense in which we will use disjunction throughout this text. The second proposition reflects the usage "either . . . or . . . , but not both." When we intend this interpretation, the phrase *but not both* will always be added.

For arbitrary propositions p and q, we will define the *disjunction of p and q*, denoted by $p + q$, to be the proposition "either p or q or both." The words *or both* are usually omitted, and the word *either* may be omitted in cases where no ambiguity results. We will require that this proposition be true whenever either one of p and q or both are true, and false only when both p and q are false.

In connection with any of these propositions, it is customary to apply the terminology introduced in Chapter 2. That is, we may speak of variables and functions in exactly the same way as before. The only change in terminology is that whenever the letters involved represent propositions, we speak of *propositional variables* and *propositional functions* rather than the more general, but equally correct, terms *Boolean variables* and *Boolean functions*.

It follows from our definitions that the negation of "*p* or *q*" is the proposition "not *p* and not *q*," which can also be stated "neither *p* nor *q*." Likewise, the negation of "*p* and *q*" is "either not *p* or not *q*." That is, the laws of De Morgan hold for propositions just as they do for sets. In symbolic form we have the following laws for propositions:

$$(p + q)' = p'q',$$
$$(pq)' = p' + q'.$$

EXAMPLE 1. Let *p* be the proposition "missiles are costly," and let *q* be the proposition "Grandma chews gum." Write in English the propositions represented by the symbols (a) $p + q'$, (b) $p'q'$, (c) $pq' + p'q$.

Solution. (a) Either missiles are costly or Grandma does not chew gum. (b) Missiles are not costly and Grandma does not chew gum. (c) Either missiles are costly and Grandma does not chew gum, or missiles are not costly and Grandma chews gum.

This last statement is not very clear, but it is difficult to avoid ambiguity in complicated sentences of this type. This difficulty is one of the primary reasons why the symbolic notations we have introduced are of value. In symbols, the proposition cannot be misunderstood.

EXERCISES

1. Which of the following sentences, or phrases, represent propositions? (Assume that all words and grammar used are free of ambiguity.)
   (a) Grass is yellow.
   (b) Beautiful white roses.
   (c) Is the number 5 a prime?
   (d) All mathematics is difficult, and some mathematics is impossible.
   (e) If dogs can bark, then no home guarded by a dog needs to fear intruders.
   (f) Give me the book.

2. Let *p* be the proposition "mathematics is easy," and let *q* be the proposition "two is less than three." Write out, in reasonable English, the propositions represented by

(a) pq (b) $p + q$ (c) $(pq)'$
(d) $(p + q)'$ (e) $p' + q'$ (f) $pq' + p'q$

3. Let p be the proposition "x is an even number," and let q be the proposition "x is the product of two integers." Translate into symbols each of the following propositions.

(a) Either x is an even number, or x is a product of two integers.

(b) x is an odd number, and x is a product of two integers.

(c) Either x is an even number and a product of integers, or x is an odd number and is not a product of integers.

(d) x is neither an even number nor a product of integers.

4. Write, in reasonable English, the negation of each of the following propositions.

(a) Ice is cold, and I am tired.

(b) Either good health is desirable, or I have been misinformed.

(c) Oranges are not suitable for use in vegetable salads.

(d) There is a number which, when added to 6, gives a sum of 13.

5. Let p, q, and r be propositions such that p is true, q is false, and r is false. Decide whether each of the following is true or false.

(a) p'　　　　　　　(b) pq　　　　　　　(c) $p + q$
(d) $(p + q) + r$　　　(e) $p' + (q + r)$　　　(f) $p' + (q + r)'$
(g) $pq + qr$　　　　　　　　　(h) $pq + p'q'$
(i) $(pq + p'q') + (p'q + pq')$　　　　(j) $(p' + q')[(p + r')(q + r)]$

6. Classify the following propositions as true for all propositions p, q, and r; false for all propositions p, q, and r; or sometimes true and sometimes false, depending upon p, q, and r.

(a) pp'　　　　　　(b) $p + p'$　　　　　(c) $(p + p')(q + r)$
(d) $(pq + pq') + (p'q + p'q')$　　　　(e) $[p + (q + r')][p' + (q + r)]$
(f) $[(p + q)(p + q')][(p' + q)(p' + q')]$

3–3 Truth tables. To show that the set of propositions and the operations of conjunction, disjunction, and negation form a Boolean algebra, it is necessary first to define the concept of *equality*. Two propositional functions g and h, each functions of the n propositional variables p_1, p_2, ..., p_n, are said to be *equal* if and only if they have the same truth value for every possible way of assigning truth values to each of the n variables. For example, if g and h are each functions of the two variables p and q, we can determine whether they are equal by checking the truth values of g and h separately for each of the four possibilities: p false and q true; p true and q false; p and q both true; and p and q both false. If the results are the same for each case, g and h are equal. If their truth values differ for any case, they are unequal.

This definition may sound strange at first, but it would be difficult to use any other definition. Certainly, a definition based on the words used to express the proposition would be impossible because there are many ways of wording a single statement in English alone, to say nothing of the possibilities if an arbitrary language is used. Similarly, there is no way in which the meaning conveyed by the proposition can be employed. Meaning is an intangible thing, impossible to treat in a precise way. The truth value, on the other hand, is specific, and by our assumption is always one of two things, truth or falsehood, for each proposition. As soon as the symbols 0 and 1 are introduced, we will see that this definition reflects the fact expressed in the corollary to Theorem 2 of Section 2–4, that a function is completely determined when its value is known for each possible assignment of 0 and 1 to the variables involved.

To complete our algebra, we will create two new propositions represented by 0 and 1, respectively. We define 0 to be a proposition that is always false, and 1 to be a proposition that is always true. The equation $p = 0$ is equivalent to the statement that p is false. Similarly, $q = 1$ is equivalent to saying that q is true.

The definition we have given for equality makes it possible to represent a function with a table of values exactly as was done in Section 2–4. The only difference is that now we have a special meaning attached to the symbols which appear in the table. These symbols stand for propositions rather than for abstract elements of an arbitrary Boolean algebra. Such a table will be termed a *truth table*. An example of such a table is Table 3–1 for the functions pq and $p + q$. In reading this table, row 3, for instance, presents the information that pq is false and $p + q$ is true if p is false and q is true.

TABLE 3–1

TRUTH TABLE FOR pq AND $p + q$

Row	p	q	pq	$p + q$
1	1	1	1	1
2	1	0	0	1
3	0	1	0	1
4	0	0	0	0

The construction of a truth table for a complicated propositional function can best be carried out in steps, using at each step the basic truth table for one of the operations (+), (·), or ('). For example, Table 3–2 shows the construction by steps of the truth table for the function $(r' + pq)'$.

If it happens that the truth table for a function contains only 1's (in the function column), we call the corresponding proposition a *tautology*. Both $p + p'$ and $pq + pq' + p'q + p'q'$ are examples of tautologies for any propositions p and q.

TABLE 3–2

CONSTRUCTION OF THE TRUTH TABLE FOR $(r' + pq)'$

Row	p	q	r	r'	pq	$r' + pq$	$(r' + pq)'$
1	1	1	1	0	1	1	0
2	1	1	0	1	1	1	0
3	1	0	1	0	0	0	1
4	1	0	0	1	0	1	0
5	0	1	1	0	0	0	1
6	0	1	0	1	0	1	0
7	0	0	1	0	0	0	1
8	0	0	0	1	0	1	0

TABLE 3–3

TRUTH TABLE SHOWING $p + qr = (p + q)(p + r)$

Row	p	q	r	qr	$p + qr$	$p + q$	$p + r$	$(p + q)(p + r)$
1	1	1	1	1	1	1	1	1
2	1	1	0	0	1	1	1	1
3	1	0	1	0	1	1	1	1
4	1	0	0	0	1	1	1	1
5	0	1	1	1	1	1	1	1
6	0	1	0	0	0	1	0	0
7	0	0	1	0	0	0	1	0
8	0	0	0	0	0	0	0	0

An illustration of the usefulness of truth tables occurs in the proof of the following theorem. From the definition of equality, it follows that two functions are equal if and only if their truth tables are identical. This fact is used in part (c) of the proof below.

THEOREM. The algebra of propositions is a Boolean algebra.

Proof. (a) That both (+) and (·) are commutative follows immediately from the definition and hence Postulate 1 (definition of Boolean algebra) holds.

(b) 0 is the identity element for the operation (+) since $0 + p$ has the same truth value as p and hence equals p. Similarly, $(1)(q)$ has the same truth value as q and hence equals q, showing that 1 is the identity for the operation of conjunction.

(c) Each operation is distributive over the other. Table 3–3 establishes one distributive law, and the other is left to the reader. (See Exercise 2 at the end of this section.)

(d) For each proposition, there is a second proposition p', the negation of p, which satisfies the relations $pp' = 0$ and $p + p' = 1$. These relations were assigned in the exercises of Section 3–2; the proof is omitted here.

We have verified all four postulates for a Boolean algebra, and with this the proof of the theorem is complete. From now on we may use without special proof any result from Chapter 2 concerning Boolean algebra.

Not only can a truth table be constructed for a given propositional function, but if it happens that a truth table is known, then the corresponding propositional function may be found in exactly the same way as a general Boolean function was constructed in Sections 2–4 and 2–5. The following hypothetical problem illustrates this procedure.

EXAMPLE. A logician was captured by a certain gang. The leader of the gang blindfolded the captive and placed him in a locked room containing two boxes. He gave the following instructions, "One box contains the key to this room, the other a poisonous snake. You are to reach into either box you choose, and if you find the key, you may use it to go free. To help you, you may ask my assistant a single question requiring a yes or no answer. However, he does not have to answer truthfully; he may lie if he chooses." After a moment of thought, the logician asked a question, reached into the box with the key, and left. What question did the logician ask so that he was certain to go free?

Solution. Let p be the proposition "the box on my left contains the key." Let q be the proposition "you are telling the truth." Suppose that we desire the answer "yes" if p is true, and "no" if p is false. The first three columns of Table 3–4 represent the possible truth values of p and q and the desired answers. The required proposition, then, must have column 4 as its truth table. To illustrate the reasoning used in forming the truth table, consider row 2. The values of p and q indicate that for this case, the key is in the left box and the man is lying. Consequently, to obtain an affirmative answer the function must have the value 0. The propositional function corresponding to this truth table is $pq + p'q'$. Hence the proper question is:

Is the proposition "the box on the left contains the key and you are telling the truth, or the box on the right contains the key and you are lying" a true proposition?

TABLE 3–4

Row	p	q	Desired answer	Truth table
1	1	1	yes	1
2	1	0	yes	0
3	0	1	no	0
4	0	0	no	1

We are assuming, of course, that the man who answers the question is intelligent enough to understand the question and that he either lies or tells the truth deliberately and does not answer in a random manner. A simpler wording is possible for the proposition, but the terminology has not yet been developed. (See the discussion of material equivalence in Section 3-5.)

EXERCISES

1. Determine which of the following are tautologies by constructing the truth table for each.

(a) $pq + p' + q'$

(b) $pq' + p'q$

(c) $p + q + p'$

(d) $(p + q)(p' + q)(p + q')$

2. Use truth tables to verify

(a) the associative law for disjunction,

(b) the associative law for conjunction,

(c) the distributive law for $(\cdot)$ over $(+)$, and

(d) the two laws of absorption.

3. Find propositional functions F_1, F_2, F_3, F_4, F_5, and F_6 with the aid of Table 3-5. Where a question mark appears in the table, either 0 or 1 may be inserted, whichever makes the resulting function the simpler. Such symbols (?) correspond to "invalid" combinations, that is, to combinations of truth values for p, q, and r which for one reason or another are known to be excluded.

TABLE 3-5

Row	p	q	r	F_1	F_2	F_3	F_4	F_5	F_6
1	1	1	1	1	0	1	1	0	?
2	1	1	0	0	0	1	0	0	?
3	1	0	1	1	0	0	1	1	?
4	1	0	0	0	1	0	1	?	?
5	0	1	1	1	0	0	1	1	0
6	0	1	0	1	0	0	0	1	0
7	0	0	1	1	0	1	1	?	0
8	0	0	0	0	1	0	1	?	1

4. In the example of this section, there is another question, having a different truth table, which the logician could have asked. What is it?

5. Construct a truth table for each of the following functions.

(a) $pqr + p'qr' + p'q'r'$

(b) $(p + q + r)(p' + q + r')(p' + q' + r')$

(c) $(p' + qr)'(pq + q'r)$

(d) $pq' + p'(qr + q'r)'$

3-4 Object logic and syntax logic. Until now, we have avoided mention of an important fact about the study of logic which causes considerable difficulty to a beginner. We have taken *proposition* as a fundamental, undefined term and defined three ways of forming propositional functions from simple propositions. The reader must be cautioned to restrict the formation of propositional functions to just those rules of combination specifically defined. The difficulty is that in discussing propositions, their algebra, and methods of deductive reasoning from these propositions, we are forced to make many statements *about* propositions. Since these statements seem to satisfy our intuitive definition of what a proposition should be, it is easy to fall into the trap of treating such statements as propositions. To clarify the situation, it is necessary to distinguish between the logic which we construct out of our propositions, called *object logic*, and the logic which we are using when we talk about the propositions, called *syntax logic*. In particular, if p and q are propositions in the object logic, p', $p + q$, and pq are also propositions in object logic. However, the statements "p is false" and "$p = q$" are propositions in syntax logic, since they are statements about the propositions.

With this warning to the student about the construction of suitable propositional functions, we will end any formal consideration of syntax logic. All remarks concerning logic will from now on refer to object logic. This restriction will, of course, limit the rigor of our treatment, but it is felt that this is excusable in an introductory text.

3-5 Material implication. Our treatment of Boolean algebra has emphasized the use of three operations, $(+)$ and $(\cdot)$, which are binary operations, and $(')$, which is often referred to as a unary operation. It has been pointed out that these operations are not independent. For example, $a + b$ may be written as $(a'b')'$. In any function, each occurrence of the symbol $(+)$ could be avoided by this replacement, giving an equivalent function expressed entirely in terms of $(\cdot)$ and $(')$. Thus we have already introduced more operations than are really necessary. In this section we will define still another operation, called *material implication*. Although the introduction of this operation is unnecessary, it is very convenient in translating worded statements into symbols because of its frequent occurrence, especially in mathematical propositions.

For any two propositions p and q, the proposition "if p then q" is familiar to all readers. Before formulating a precise definition in symbols, let us consider what meaning seems reasonable for this proposition. Often in the statement of a mathematical theorem involving this proposition, p and q are related in such a way that q may be systematically derived from p. To impart such a meaning in the algebra of propositions is impossible because our definition of equality allows us to consider only the truth value of propositions, not their meaning. We must limit our consideration to truth-value properties, then. It is intuitively evident that if p is true and q is true, we should call the proposition "if p then q" true, and we would obviously call it false if p were true but q were false. These are the two cases which arise most commonly in mathematics, but they do not cover all possibilities. We will consider the implication true in each case in which the proposition p is false, which completes the description of the proposition.

We will define the relation →, called *material implication*, by the equation $p \rightarrow q = p' + q$ for arbitrary propositions p and q. In the proposition $p \rightarrow q$, p is called the *antecedent* and q is called the *consequent* of the implication. This definition reflects the properties discussed in the preceding paragraph. Table 3–6 tabulates the truth values of this new function.

TABLE 3–6

TRUTH TABLE FOR $p \rightarrow q$

Row	p	q	$p \rightarrow q$
1	1	1	1
2	1	0	0
3	0	1	1
4	0	0	1

Remember that the word *implies* does not mean that q can be logically deduced from p. Nothing more should be read into $p \rightarrow q$ than "either not p or q." For example, the proposition "if 6 is an odd integer, then the moon is made of green cheese" is a true proposition because the antecedent is false.

We will introduce another relation that occurs frequently in mathematics. For any two propositions p and q, the relation ↔, called *material equivalence*, is defined by the equation $p \leftrightarrow q = (p \rightarrow q)(q \rightarrow p)$. The proposition $p \leftrightarrow q$ is usually read "p if and only if q." In general, $p \leftrightarrow q$, for compound or simple propositions p and q, is a true proposition in exactly those cases in which $p = q$. The difference in notation is necessary to distinguish between $p \leftrightarrow q$, which is a proposition, and $p = q$, which is not a proposition but a statement *about* propositions.

Table 3–7 contains several abbreviated sentences and their translations into symbolic notation. For our purpose, these will serve as definitions of the connectives used.

Related to any implication $p \rightarrow q$ are three other implications of frequent use in the statement of theorems. The *converse* of $p \rightarrow q$ is $q \rightarrow p$; the *inverse* of $p \rightarrow q$ is $p' \rightarrow q'$; and the *contrapositive* of $p \rightarrow q$

TABLE 3–7

If p then q	$p \to q$
p if q	$q \to p$
p only if q	$p \to q$
p unless q	$q' \to p$
p is a sufficient condition for q	$p \to q$
p is a necessary condition for q	$q \to p$
A sufficient condition for p is q	$q \to p$
A necessary condition for p is q	$p \to q$
In order that p it is sufficient that q	$q \to p$
In order that p it is necessary that q	$p \to q$
p if and only if q	$p \leftrightarrow q$
p is a necessary and sufficient condition for q	$p \leftrightarrow q$

TABLE 3–8

IMPLICATION, CONVERSE, INVERSE, AND CONTRAPOSITIVE

Row	p	q	$p \to q$	$q \to p$	$p' \to q'$	$q' \to p'$
1	1	1	1	1	1	1
2	1	0	0	1	1	0
3	0	1	1	0	0	1
4	0	0	1	1	1	1

is $q' \to p'$. Of these, the original implication and its contrapositive are equal to each other, and the inverse and converse are equal. Table 3–8 establishes these statements.

From the definition of $p \to q$ and from De Morgan's law, we see that the negation of $p \to q$ is given by $(p \to q)' = (p' + q)' = pq'$. In words, "it is false that p implies q" may also be stated "p and not q."

EXAMPLE 1. Let p be the proposition "eight is an even number," and let q be the proposition "candy is sweet." Form, in words, (a) the implication $p \to q$, (b) its converse, (c) its inverse, (d) its contrapositive, and (e) its negation.

Solution:

(a) If 8 is an even number, then candy is sweet.
(b) If candy is sweet, then 8 is an even number.
(c) If 8 is an odd number, then candy is not sweet.
(d) If candy is not sweet, then 8 is an odd number.
(e) Eight is an even number, and candy is not sweet.

EXAMPLE 2. Designate suitable simple propositions p and q and translate the following propositional functions into symbols.

(a) If lemons are expensive and sugar is cheap, then sour lemonade is rarely seen.

(b) Sour lemonade is often seen unless sugar is cheap.

(c) A necessary condition for lemons to be cheap is that sugar is expensive.

(d) Sour lemonade is rarely seen only if sugar is cheap.

Solution. Let m be the proposition "lemons are expensive," let s be the proposition "sugar is cheap," and let r be the proposition "sour lemonade is rarely seen." Then the symbolic translations are (a) $ms \to r$, (b) $s' \to r'$, (c) $m' \to s'$, and (d) $r \to s$.

EXERCISES

1. Prove that each of the following is a tautology.

(a) $p \to p$ (b) $p(p \to q) \to q$ (c) $p' \to (p \to q)$

(d) $[(p \to q)(q \to r)] \to (p \to r)$

(e) $(ab + bc + ca) \leftrightarrow (a + b)(b + c)(c + a)$

(f) $(p \to q) \to [(p + qr) \leftrightarrow q(p + r)]$

2. Write in words the converse, inverse, contrapositive, and negation of the implication "if 2 is less than 3, then $\frac{1}{3}$ is less than $\frac{1}{2}$."

3. (a) Write in words the converse, inverse, contrapositive, and negation of the implication "if water is wet and grass is blue, then either math is easy or logic is nonsense." (b) Describe a suitable notation for the simple propositions involved in the proposition in (a), and write in symbols each of the propositions asked for.

4. Show that the question asked by the logician in the example of Section 3–3 is equivalent to the question "does the box on the left contain the key if and only if you are telling the truth?"

5. Let p denote the proposition "money is evil," let q denote the proposition "wise men are poor," and let r denote the proposition "beggars are failures." Translate each of the following propositions into symbols.

(a) Wise men are poor only if money is evil.

(b) Money is evil unless wise men are poor.

(c) That beggars are failures is a sufficient condition that money is evil.

(d) A necessary condition for money to be evil is that beggars are failures.

(e) Money is evil and beggars are failures if wise men are poor.

(f) Unless beggars are failures, wise men are not poor and money is not evil.

6. Write in reasonable English the negation of each of the following propositions.

(a) It will rain unless the barometer rises.

(b) I grow fat only if I eat too much.

(c) A necessary condition that two triangles are equivalent is that they have the same area.

(d) In order to live well, it is sufficient to be wealthy.

3–6 Truth sets for propositions. In considering any problem, either logical or mathematical, it is important to have a thorough understanding of the logical possibilities connected with the problem. The consideration in this section is undertaken to determine the truth or falsity of statements related to a problem. As an illustration of what we mean by *logical possibilities*, the truth-table method for analyzing a compound proposition is nothing more than a tabulation of the various logical possibilities for the simple propositions involved. However, the truth table is not always a sufficiently refined analysis to serve the purposes of the problem.

For example, consider the following proposition concerning integers a and b. "Either a is not less than b or b is not less than a." Intuitively, it is evident that this proposition is a tautology. Yet if we designate by p the proposition "a is less than b," and by q the proposition "b is less than a," and construct the truth table for the compound proposition (Table 3–9), we fail to establish this fact because 0 appears in row 1 of the table.

TABLE 3–9

TRUTH TABLE FOR $p' + q'$

Row	p	q	p'	q'	$p' + q'$
1	1	1	0	0	0
2	1	0	0	1	1
3	0	1	1	0	1
4	0	0	1	1	1

The trouble is that although truth tables are adequate for considering the logical possibilities for functions of propositional variables alone, they are usually not adequate for the treatment of specific propositions, that is, for functions involving constants. In the above example, consideration of the propositions p and q reveals that it is impossible for p and q to be true simultaneously. Hence row 1 of the table simply does not apply, and the proposition is a tautology.

The propositions considered above furnish an example of *related propositions*. Many other relations are possible between two or more propositions, each identified by the fact that one or more rows of a corresponding truth table do not represent possible truth values for the propositions. It is not our purpose to investigate systematically all such relationships, but the example serves to illustrate a need for discussing the matter of logical possibilities, at least in a general way.

Another instance where a discussion of logical possibilities is important arises in the following example.

EXAMPLE. A bowl contains fifteen marbles of which five are white, five are red, and five are blue. Two marbles are drawn, one at a time, from the bowl. Discuss the truth value of the proposition "one white and one blue marble are drawn." (Such propositions are important in studying probability theory.)

Solution. To analyze the truth properties of the proposition, it is helpful to consider the logical possibilities associated with the situation to which the proposition refers. These are tabulated in Table 3–10. It appears that in cases 6 and 8 the proposition is true and in all others it is false.

TABLE 3–10

Case	First drawing	Second drawing	Truth value
1	red	red	0
2	red	white	0
3	red	blue	0
4	white	red	0
5	white	white	0
6	white	blue	1
7	blue	red	0
8	blue	white	1
9	blue	blue	0

In this example, nine cases were considered as logical possibilities. If, however, the white balls were numbered and the proposition had been "white ball number 2 was drawn after a red ball," it would have been necessary to consider more than nine cases as logical possibilities. The number and nature of logical possibilities associated with a proposition or set of propositions depend on the propositions under consideration, and no general formula or method can be given. If the propositions involve only variables, a truth table will suffice; in most other cases it will not.

The primary reason for discussing logical possibilities for propositions is to help in bridging the gap that exists intuitively between the algebra of sets and the algebra of logic. We may assign to any set of propositions under discussion a universal set whose elements are the logical possibilities for the set of propositions. This can usually be done in many ways. When it is required to specify these elements precisely, we will choose the most convenient set of possibilities that have the following two properties.

(1) The possibilities listed are such that in any conceivable circumstance, one and only one of the possibilities is the case.

(2) The possibilities are such that the truth value of each proposition can be determined by any one of the possibilities.

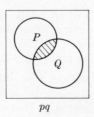   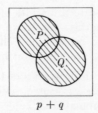   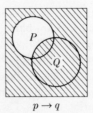

pq   p + q   p → q

FIG. 3–1.   Truth sets for compound propositions.

Next, a subset of this universal set is assigned to each proposition so that the subset consists of exactly those possibilities for which the proposition is true. This set is called the *truth set* for the proposition.

It should be clear that the truth set for a propositional function is uniquely determined by the truth sets for the simple propositions which make it up. We may even represent truth sets abstractly by Venn diagrams, exactly as we represented sets in Chapter 1. This use of truth sets can be a very helpful aid to understanding logic. It also illustrates the strong relationship between the algebra of sets and the algebra of logic. Figure 3–1 uses Venn diagrams to show the truth sets for pq, $p + q$, and $p \rightarrow q$ in terms of the truth sets for p and q. P and Q represent the truth sets for the propositions p and q, and the shaded areas represent the truth sets for the compound propositions.

EXERCISES

1. A child has three coins, no two alike, and the total value is less than \$1. List the ten logical possibilities suitable for considering the following propositions, and number them in order of increasing total value. List, by number, the possibilities for which each of the propositions is true. (That is, give the truth set for each proposition.)

(a) The child has a nickel.   (b) The child has at least 75¢.

(c) The child has a nickel or a dime.

(d) The child has neither a quarter nor a half dollar.

2. How many logical possibilities are there if it is known that a child has three coins, none larger than a quarter, two or more of which may be alike? Assume that all propositions involved refer only to the total monetary value of the coins.

3. Are the propositions "Pat is a girl" and "Pat is a boy" related? How?

4. A die is thrown twice. Describe a set of logical possibilities suitable for considering (simultaneously) the following three propositions.

(a) The first throw comes up 6.   (b) The two throws total 5.

(c) The first throw comes up in an even number, and the second in an odd number.

5. What are the truth sets for each of the propositions in Exercise 4?

6. What is the maximum number of propositions among the following set which could be simultaneously true?

(a) Ice cream is delicious.

(b) Ice cream is cold.

(c) Ice cream is delicious only if it is cold.

(d) Ice cream is delicious if and only if it is cold.

(e) Either ice cream is not cold or it is not delicious.

(f) Either ice cream is cold or it is delicious, but not both.

7. For each of the following, draw a Venn diagram showing the truth sets for p, q, and r as the interiors of three circles, and shade the area corresponding to the truth sets for the given propositions.

(a) $p \rightarrow q'$ (b) $(p + r) \rightarrow q$

(c) $p \leftrightarrow qr$ (d) $(p + q)(pq)'$

8. Two or more propositions are said to be *inconsistent* if they cannot all be true at the same time. What does this imply about their truth sets?

9. Explain why the truth set for any tautology is the universal set of all logical possibilities.

10. Let P be the truth set for the proposition p, and let Q be the truth set for the proposition q. Show that $p \rightarrow q$ is a tautology if and only if $P \subseteq Q$.

3–7 Quantifiers. In our consideration of logic, we have talked about propositions and the ways in which they can be combined to form new propositions, but have given little or no attention to the way in which simple propositions are constructed. Discussion of words and phrases within propositions will, for the most part, be outside the scope of this text. However, to understand some very important types of mathematical propositions, it is essential to mention one such topic, namely, the construction and meaning of propositions containing *quantifiers*. The following are examples of propositions which contain quantifiers:

> some men are wealthy;
> all men are prejudiced;
> no man is patient.

The words *some*, *all*, and *no* are quantifiers. They tell us "how many" of a certain set of things is being considered. Many statements do not specifically contain quantifiers although quantification is implied. Consider the following mathematical propositions in the form of equations:

$$x^2 + 4x = 7,$$
$$x^2 - 4 = (x + 2)(x - 2).$$

The first is true in the sense that for *at least one* number x, $x^2 + 4x = 7$, and the second is true in the more general sense that for *every* number x,

$x^2 - 4 = (x + 2)(x - 2)$. The first equation could be proven false only by showing that no number x satisfies the equation, but the second could be shown to be false by exhibiting a single number x which fails to satisfy the equation. It is important, then, to distinguish carefully between these types of propositions.

We define the symbol $\forall_x p$ to mean that for every x in a given set, the proposition p is true. $\forall_x$ is called the *universal quantifier* of the variable x and is usually read "for all x" or "for every x." We will define the symbol $\exists_x p$ to mean that for one or more elements x of a certain set of elements, the proposition p is true. $\exists_x$ is called the *existential quantifier* of the variable x and is usually read "there exists an x such that p" or "for at least one x, p" or, less precisely, "for some x, p."

Since each quantifier refers to a particular set of permissible values for the variable x, this set must be mentioned. Frequently, this set is described in a sentence preceding the proposition that contains the quantifier, although the set may be included in the proposition itself. For instance, the propositions above may be written in any of the following ways:

there exists a number x such that $x^2 + 4x = 7$;
for all numbers x, $x^2 - 4 = (x + 2)(x - 2)$.

Alternatively, we may write:

$\exists_x p$, where x belongs to the set of all numbers
and where p is the proposition $x^2 + 4x = 7$;

$\forall_x q$, where x belongs to the set of all numbers
and where q is the proposition $x^2 - 4 = (x + 2)(x - 2)$.

Still other forms are:

if x is a number, $\exists_x(x^2 + 4x = 7)$;
if x is a number, $\forall_x[x^2 - 4 = (x + 2)(x - 2)]$.

It is important to know how the negations of propositions involving quantifiers are formed. A little reflection will justify the following formulas:

$$(\exists_x p)' = \forall_x p',$$
$$(\forall_x p)' = \exists_x p'.$$

Since the symbols for quantification cannot be manipulated in the algebra of propositions, they will not be used to any great extent in this text. They are introduced primarily to specify the rules for negation. Ordinarily, we will continue to denote propositions, quantified or not, by single letters. However, to word a given symbolic expression in proper

English, it is necessary to understand the nature of any quantifiers which are involved. A third quantifier should be mentioned because of its frequent occurrence. The following illustration will serve. The proposition "no man is patient" contains the quantifier *no*. We will interpret this as being equivalent to the proposition "all men are impatient" or, to put it in symbolic form, $\forall_x p'$, where x is a man and p is the proposition "x is patient."

EXERCISES

1. Let p be the proposition "x is wealthy," and let q be the proposition "y is married." Further, assume that both x and y represent members of the set of all men. Write the following propositions in English. (Do not use $\exists$, $\forall$, or x in your statements.)

(a) $\exists_x p$
(b) $\forall_x p + \exists_y q$
(c) $\forall_x p'$
(d) $(\forall_x p)(\exists_y q)$

2. In the following, let x, y, and z refer to real numbers. Rewrite each of the propositions in words without the use of the symbol $\exists$ or $\forall$.

(a) $\exists_x (x > 7)$
(b) $\forall_x (x^2 \geq 0)$
(c) $\forall_x \exists_y (x + y = 7)$
(d) $\exists_y \forall_x (xy + x = 3x)$

3. Form the negation of each of the following.

(a) All Americans are crazy.
(b) All men are honest or some man is a thief.
(c) There is at least one person who is happy all the time.
(d) If the number x is less than 10, then there is a number y such that $x^2 + y^2 - 100$ is positive.
(e) The corresponding sides of two triangles are equal only if the triangles are congruent.
(f) For every man there is at least one woman who despises him.

3–8 Valid arguments. The central problem in symbolic logic is the investigation of the process of reasoning. In mathematics, as in every deductive science, there are no assertions of "absolute" truth. Rather, a certain set of propositions is assumed without proof, and from this set, other propositions are derived by logical reasoning. For example, when we assert the truth of the Pythagorean theorem, we mean simply that it can be deduced from the axioms of the Euclidean geometry of the plane. It is not true, for instance, for triangles on the surface of a sphere. We now proceed to investigate those processes which will be accepted as valid in the derivation of a proposition, called the *conclusion*, from other given propositions, called the *premises*.

We define an *argument* to be a process by which a conclusion is formed from given premises. An argument is *valid* if and only if the conjunction of the premises implies the conclusion. That is, the argument which yields a conclusion r from premises $p_1, p_2, \ldots, p_n$ is valid if and only if the proposition $(p_1 p_2 \cdots p_n) \to r$ is a tautology. In general, there are three ways to check the validity of a given argument. The first is to check it directly from the definition by using a truth table; that is, for the argument above, the truth-table method is used to show that $(p_1 p_2 \cdots p_n) \to r$ is a tautology. The second method is to show that the proposition $(p_1 p_2 \cdots p_n) \to r$ can be reduced to 1, using the standard methods of simplification. The third, and often the simplest of the three, is to reduce the argument to a series of arguments each of which is known to be valid as a result of previous checking. Two of the most frequently used valid arguments are the *rule of detachment* (also called *modus ponens*) and the *law of syllogism*. The rule of detachment is given by the form

$$p$$
$$\underline{p \to q}$$
$$q.$$

We will use this schematic arrangement in stating all our arguments. The premise, or premises, will be listed first and the conclusion will follow beneath a horizontal line. Reasons or explanations may be written to the right of each proposition.

The *law of syllogism* is given by the form

$$p \to q$$
$$\underline{q \to r}$$
$$p \to r.$$

The validity of this argument, as well as of *modus ponens*, may be easily checked by either of the first two methods previously mentioned.

It is important to note that an argument is valid or invalid independently of the truth or falsity of the conclusion. For example, consider the following two arguments. The first is valid although the conclusion is false, and the second is invalid although the conclusion is true.

Valid:

If ice is warm, then snow is black.
Ice is warm.

Snow is black.

Invalid:

5 is an odd integer.
If 4 is an even integer, then 5 is an odd integer.

4 is an even integer.

In addition to the rule of *modus ponens*, and the law of syllogism, the valid argument forms in Table 3–11 have either been checked in previous problems or can readily be verified.

TABLE 3–11

FORMS OF VALID ARGUMENT

Form 1	Form 2	Form 3	Form 4	Form 5	Form 6
p q $\overline{}$ pq	pq $\overline{}$ p	p' $\overline{}$ $p \to q$	$p + q$ p' $\overline{}$ q	p $\overline{}$ $p + q$	q $\overline{}$ $p \to q$

In checking the validity of any argument, we will also assume that it is permissible to use either of the following rules of substitution.

RULE 1. Any valid argument which involves a propositional variable will remain valid if *every* occurrence of a given variable is replaced by a specific proposition.

RULE 2. Any valid argument will remain valid if *any* occurrence of a proposition is replaced by an equivalent proposition.

From the definition of a valid argument, it follows at once that in addition to any given premises, we may use as a premise any tautology in the algebra of propositions.

In checking a given argument for validity, if it is found or suspected that the argument is invalid, a proof of invalidity can be given more easily than by constructing the entire truth table related to the argument. It is sufficient to exhibit a particular set of truth values for the propositions involved for which the premises are all true and the conclusion is false. This does nothing more than demonstrate that one row in the truth table, if constructed, would contain a 0 and hence the argument is invalid.

EXAMPLE 1. Show that the following argument is valid:

$$p$$
$$p \to q$$
$$q \to r$$
$$\overline{}$$
$$r.$$

First solution: We construct the truth table for the function

$$f = [p(p \to q)(q \to r)] \to r.$$

(See Table 3–12.) Since the f column contains only 1's, the argument is valid.

TABLE 3–12

TRUTH TABLE FOR THE ARGUMENT OF EXAMPLE 1

Row	p	q	r	$p \to q$	$q \to r$	$p(p \to q)(q \to r)$	f
1	1	1	1	1	1	1	1
2	1	1	0	1	0	0	1
3	1	0	1	0	1	0	1
4	1	0	0	0	1	0	1
5	0	1	1	1	1	0	1
6	0	1	0	1	0	0	1
7	0	0	1	1	1	0	1
8	0	0	0	1	1	0	1

Second solution: Consider the function f as above:

$$
\begin{aligned}
f &= [p(p \to q)(q \to r)] \to r \\
&= [p(p' + q)(q' + r)]' + r \\
&= p' + pq' + qr' + r \\
&= p' + q' + r' + r \\
&= 1.
\end{aligned}
$$

Since f reduces to 1, this also shows that the argument is valid.

Third solution: Consider the following sequence of arguments:

p	a premise
$p \to q$	a premise
q	*modus ponens*
$q \to r$	a premise
$r.$	*modus ponens*

This sequence of valid arguments shows again, and with less work than either of the first two methods, that the given argument was valid.

EXAMPLE 2. Check the validity of the argument

$$
\begin{aligned}
p &\to q \\
r &\to q' \\
\hline
p &\to r'.
\end{aligned}
$$

Solution: The argument

$$
\begin{aligned}
p &\to q \\
q &\to r' \\
\hline
p &\to r'
\end{aligned}
$$

is valid by the law of syllogism. Since $r \to q'$ is equivalent to $q \to r'$, an application of Substitution Rule 2 completes the proof.

EXAMPLE 3. Show that the following argument is not valid:

$$p$$
$$q' + r$$
$$p' \rightarrow q$$

$$r.$$

Solution: If p is true, q is false, and r is false, then each of the premises is true but the conclusion is false. Hence the argument is invalid.

EXERCISES

1. Show, using the definition of valid argument, that the rule of detachment and the law of syllogism represent valid arguments.

2. Show that the following argument is valid by each of the three methods illustrated in Example 1:

$$q$$
$$q \rightarrow r$$

$$p \rightarrow r.$$

3. Check the validity of each of the following arguments. Show proof for your answers.

(a) pq
$p' \rightarrow q$

q'

(b) $p \rightarrow q$
q'

p'

(c) p
$p + q$
$(p + q) \rightarrow r$
$r \rightarrow s$

s

(d) r
$p \leftrightarrow q'$
$q \rightarrow r$

p

(e) p
$p \rightarrow [q \rightarrow (r \rightarrow s)]$

s

(f) pr
$(p \rightarrow q) \rightarrow (r \rightarrow s)$

s

(g) $[(p \rightarrow q) \rightarrow r] \rightarrow s$
r

s

4. Check the validity of the following arguments. Show proof with the use of symbolic notation.

(a) $x^2 = y^2$ only if $x = y$
$x = y$

$x^2 = y^2$

(b) Grass is green.

If grass is blue and ice is wet, then there are alligators on the moon.

(c) Mathematics is easy unless the instructor is dull.
Mathematics is easy only if calculus is not to be feared.

If calculus is to be feared, then the instructor is dull.

5. Given the following statements, as premises, all referring to an arbitrary meal:

(a) If he takes coffee, he doesn't drink milk.
(b) He eats crackers only if he drinks milk.
(c) He doesn't take soup unless he eats crackers.
(d) At noon today, he had coffee.

Is it possible to make a conclusion about whether he took soup at noon today? If so, what is the correct conclusion?

6. A mathematical theorem often consists of an implication $p \rightarrow q$ between related statements. Discuss this relation in cases for which the theorem is true.

3–9 Indirect proofs. The simplest indirect proof is an application of the fact that any implication $p \rightarrow q$ is equivalent to its contrapositive $q' \rightarrow p'$. For example, suppose that we wish to establish the implication "if x^2 is an odd number, then x is an odd number." The following is an indirect proof. Assume that $x = 2n$ is an even number. Then $x^2 = 4n^2$, an even number, and this completes the proof.

More generally, we define an *indirect proof* of the validity of a given argument to be any valid argument which has for premises one or more premises of the given argument and the negation of the given conclusion, and for a conclusion either the negation of a given premise or the negation of any known true proposition. For example, the argument with premises $p_1, p_2, \ldots, p_n$ and conclusion q is valid if we can show that a second argument with premises $q', p_2, p_3, \ldots, p_n$ and conclusion p_1' is valid.

Any of the arguments used as indirect proofs and according to the definition are equivalent to the given argument. While we will not prove this statement in general, the method of proof for any given case is illustrated by the following example.

EXAMPLE 1. In attempting to show that the argument

$$p$$
$$q$$
$$\overline{}$$
$$r$$

is valid, suppose that the argument

$$r'$$
$$p$$
$$\overline{}$$
$$q'$$

has been shown to be valid. This is an example of an indirect proof. To show that this is equivalent to the direct method, we note that the validity of the second argument means that $r'p \rightarrow q'$ is a tautology. But $r'p \rightarrow q'$ is equal to $r + p' + q'$, and this in turn is equal to $pq \rightarrow r$, which must also be a tautology. Hence, the original argument is valid by the definition of validity.

EXAMPLE 2. Test the following argument for validity:

$$p$$
$$pq \rightarrow r + s$$
$$q$$
$$s'$$
___
$$r.$$

Solution. We will take as premises for the indirect proof all given premises except s', and the negation of the conclusion, r'. The indirect argument, in steps, follows:

p	a premise
q	a premise
pq	valid conclusion by Form 1
$pq \rightarrow r + s$	a premise
$r + s$	valid conclusion by *modus ponens*
r'	a premise
$s.$	valid conclusion by Form 4

But this conclusion is the negation of the premise s', hence the given argument is valid.

A special type of proof arises in attempting to show that a given implication is false. The obvious method is to prove that the negation of the given implication is true. However, if the implication concerns a property of a set of objects, it is often easy to disprove the implication by exhibiting a specific element of the set for which the proposition is false. Such a proof is called a proof by *counterexample*.

EXERCISES

1. Check the validity of the following. Use first a direct method and, second, an indirect method to prove the validity of each valid argument.

(a) $p \rightarrow q$
$r \rightarrow q'$
___
$p \rightarrow r'$

(b) p
q
$p' \rightarrow r$
$q \rightarrow r'$
___
r'

(c) p
q
$pq \rightarrow r + q$
$p + q \rightarrow rq$
___
r

(d) $ab \rightarrow cd$
$b' + d'$
___
$a' + b'$

2. Prove that the following are valid arguments. (Some work best by the indirect method.)

(a) $q \rightarrow p$
$q + s$
s'
___
p

(b) p
$p' + s' \rightarrow p'r'$
___
s

(c) $r \rightarrow q'$
$p \rightarrow q$
$r' \rightarrow s$
___
$p \rightarrow s$

(d) $p \rightarrow r$

$(p \rightarrow q) \rightarrow s$

s'

---

r

(e) $(p \rightarrow q) \rightarrow [p' \rightarrow (q \rightarrow r)]$

p'

$q \rightarrow r$

(f) $p \rightarrow [q \rightarrow (r \rightarrow s)]$

pqr

---

s

(g) $[(p \rightarrow q) \rightarrow r] \rightarrow s$

s'

p

---

q

(h) $a \rightarrow bc$

$b + d \rightarrow e$

$d + a$

---

e

3. Prove that the statement "if n is an integer, then $n^2 - n + 41$ is a prime number" is false. Use a proof by counterexample.

*3–10 Functionally complete sets of operations. A set of operations is *functionally complete* provided every propositional function can be expressed entirely in terms of operations in the set. To exhibit a functionally complete set, we recall that every propositional function has a truth table. Further, every truth table corresponds to a unique expression in disjunctive (or conjunctive) normal form, involving only the operations $(+)$, $(\cdot)$, and $(')$. Hence the set $\{+, \cdot, '\}$ is functionally complete.

Since the proposition pq is equal to the proposition $(p' + q')'$ by the law of De Morgan, it is possible to replace each occurrence of conjunction in any propositional function with an equivalent expression involving only $(+)$ and $(')$. This shows that $\{+, '\}$ is a functionally complete set of operations. Other functionally complete sets are $\{\cdot, '\}$ and $\{\rightarrow, '\}$.

It is possible to define a single operation which constitutes a functionally complete set. Suppose that we define $p \downarrow q$ by Table 3–13. This

TABLE 3–13

DEFINITION OF $p \downarrow q$

p	q	$p \downarrow q$
1	1	0
1	0	1
0	1	1
0	0	1

---

* This section may be omitted without loss of continuity.

operation can be interpreted as "not both p and q." To see how this operation alone constitutes a functionally complete set, consider Table 3–14. From this table, we observe that $p' = p \downarrow p$ and $p + q =$

TABLE 3–14

p	q	$p \downarrow p$	$q \downarrow q$	$(p \downarrow p) \downarrow (q \downarrow q)$
1	1	0	0	1
1	0	0	1	1
0	1	1	0	1
0	0	1	1	0

$(p \downarrow p) \downarrow (q \downarrow q)$. But we have shown that every propositional function can be expressed in terms of $(+)$ and $(')$. Each occurrence of $(+)$ and $(')$ may be replaced by the equivalent expression in terms of $(\downarrow)$, and hence every propositional function can be written entirely in terms of the operation $(\downarrow)$. The operation $(\downarrow)$ is one of two operations known as *Sheffer stroke functions*. The other is given in Problem 5 below.

EXERCISES

1. (a) Prove that $\{\cdot, '\}$ is a functionally complete set. (b) Prove that $\{\rightarrow, '\}$ is a functionally complete set.

2. Prove that $\{+, \cdot\}$ is not a functionally complete set.

3. Express $p \rightarrow q$, and pq in terms of $(\downarrow)$.

4. Express the propositional function $(p + q') \rightarrow pr$

(a) in terms of $(+)$ and $(')$ only.
(b) in terms of $(\cdot)$ and $(')$ only.
(c) in terms of $(\rightarrow)$ and $(')$ only.
(d) in terms of $(\downarrow)$ only.

5. The second Sheffer stroke function, $(\uparrow)$, is given by Table 3–15.

TABLE 3–15

p	q	$p \uparrow q$
1	1	0
1	0	0
0	1	0
0	0	1

(a) Choose suitable words to express this connective in English.
(b) Draw a Venn diagram showing the truth set for $p \uparrow q$.
(c) Express p', pq, $p + q$, and $p \rightarrow q$ in terms of $(\uparrow)$ only.

6. Another relation often used in logic corresponds to the connective "either . . . or . . . , but not both." The symbol ($\pm$) is called *exclusive disjunction* and defined by $p \pm q = pq' + p'q$.

(a) Construct a truth table for exclusive disjunction.

(b) Draw a Venn diagram to illustrate the truth set for $p \pm q$ in terms of the truth sets for p and q.

(c) Could the operation of exclusive disjunction be used instead of the operation of disjunction in the disjunctive normal form of a function? Explain.

(d) Write the following functions in terms of ($\pm$), ($\cdot$), and ($'$) only.

(1) $p + q$ (2) $p \to q$

(3) $pq' + p'q'$ (4) $(p + q)(p' + q')$

*3–11 Special problems. This section is devoted to examples of the methods we have derived so far in the treatment of two types of logical problems. Although it is a repetition of material already presented, specific illustrations may help the student to realize the flexibility of Boolean algebra and strengthen his ability to successfully treat problems of an applied nature. The first problem is of a type which arises naturally in writing or interpreting legal documents and insurance contracts. Although the examples given in this text are nonsensical, the methods apply equally well to important problems of a more realistic nature.

EXAMPLE 1. The irascible husband carried his new bride across the threshold and then remarked, "We'll get along fine, Honey, provided you observe the following rules:

"(a) At any meal when you do not serve bread, you must serve ice cream.

"(b) If you serve both bread and ice cream at the same meal, then you must not serve dill pickles.

"(c) If dill pickles are served, or bread is not served, then ice cream must not be served."

The bride was willing to comply, but was a bit confused about how to remember these somewhat involved rules. The problem is to simplify the rules.

First solution. Stating three conditions which must hold simultaneously is equivalent to stating that the conjunction of the three propositions represented must hold. We will form this conjunction and simplify it to an equivalent proposition which is easier to interpret than the original set of three. Denote the simple propositions involved as follows:

b: Bread is to be served.

i: Ice cream is to be served.

p: Dill pickles are to be served.

---

* This section may be omitted without loss of continuity.

Now the rules may be translated into the following symbolic expressions:

$$b' \to i \qquad \text{or, equivalently,} \qquad b + i, \tag{a}$$
$$bi \to p' \qquad \text{or, equivalently,} \qquad b' + i' + p', \tag{b}$$
$$p + b' \to i' \qquad \text{or, equivalently,} \qquad p'b + i'. \tag{c}$$

Forming the conjunction of these propositions, we have

$$\begin{aligned}
(b + i)(b' + i' + p')(p'b + i') &= (bi + bp' + b'i + ip')(p'b + i') \\
&= bi' + bp' \\
&= b(ip)'.
\end{aligned}$$

Hence the single rule "always serve bread, and never serve ice cream and pickles together" is equivalent to the three given rules.

Although the preceding method is straightforward, it does not fit in very well with the methods introduced in Chapter 1 for dealing with conditional equations, even though the problems are essentially the same. To make this clear, we note that stating a proposition as a premise is equivalent to an assertion that it is true. That is, instead of merely listing $p \to q$, we might equally well write $p \to q = 1$, or $p' + q = 1$, or $pq' = 0$. The same information is conveyed in each case, although the last three forms are not propositions. This suggests an alternate solution for Example 1.

Second solution. Using the same notation as before, we now translate the three rules as follows:

$$b'i' = 0, \tag{a}$$
$$bip = 0, \tag{b}$$
$$(p + b')i = 0. \tag{c}$$

Combining these equations, we obtain

$$b'i' + bip + (p + b')i = 0$$

or, equivalently,

$$b' + ip = 0.$$

Now, taking complements of both sides, we have

$$b(ip)' = 1,$$

and this leads to the same final rule as before.

Since $p \to q$ is equivalent to $pq' = 0$, Theorem 10 of Section 2–3 on the transitivity of $\subseteq$ has a corollary in the algebra of propositions. This corollary could be worded, *if $p \to q$ and $q \to r$ are known to be true, then it follows that $p \to r$ is true.* This is equivalent to the statement that $[(p \to q)(q \to r)] \to (p \to r)$ is a tautology, and hence to the valid argument called the *law of syllogism.* Sets of premises from which a valid conclusion may be drawn by more than one application of the law of syllogism are called *sorites*. Syllogisms and sorites may be solved either by using the notations of the algebra of sets, or by using those of the algebra of propositions.

EXAMPLE 2. Suppose that it is desired to form a conclusion from the following premises:

(a) A grouper is a fish.
(b) If an animal is a fish, then it swims well.
(c) An animal is clumsy only if it does not swim well.
(d) All animals are either clumsy or agile.

First solution. Using the terminology of sets, we define the universal set to be the set of all animals and define subsets as follows:

G: the set of all groupers,
F: the set of all fish,
S: the set of all animals that swim well,
C: the set of all clumsy animals,
A: the set of agile animals.

The translations into symbols are then

$$G \subseteq F, \tag{a}$$
$$F \subseteq S, \tag{b}$$
$$C \subseteq S' \quad \text{or} \quad S \subseteq C', \tag{c}$$
$$C + A = 1 \quad \text{or} \quad C' \subseteq A. \tag{d}$$

Hence we conclude that $G \subseteq A$ or, in words, "all groupers are agile." This is called the *major conclusion*. There are other conclusions, called *minor conclusions* that might also be drawn; for instance, "groupers swim well."

Second solution. Using the terminology of propositions, define propositional symbols as follows:

g: This animal is a grouper.
f: This animal is a fish.
s: This animal swims well.
c: This animal is clumsy.
a: This animal is agile.

The translations are

$$g \rightarrow f, \tag{a}$$
$$f \rightarrow s, \tag{b}$$
$$c \rightarrow s' \quad \text{or, equivalently,} \quad s \rightarrow c', \tag{c}$$
$$c + a \quad \text{or, equivalently,} \quad c' \rightarrow a. \tag{d}$$

From these we conclude that $g \rightarrow a$ or, in words, "if this animal is a grouper, then it is agile." This result is the same as before even though the wording is slightly different.

1. Find the major conclusion from the following premises. Set the problem up twice, once in the terminology of the algebra of sets, and again in the terminology of the algebra of propositions. (From Lewis Carroll.)

(a) All ducks in this village which are branded "B" belong to Mrs. Bond.
(b) Ducks in this village never wear lace collars, unless they are branded "B".
(c) Mrs. Bond has no gray ducks in this village.

2. Do the same for the following set of premises. Assume that a *desk* is a type of box. (From Lewis Carroll.)

(a) There is no box of mine here that I dare open.
(b) My writing desk is made of rosewood.
(c) All my boxes are painted, except what are here.
(d) All my rosewood boxes are unpainted.
(e) There is no box of mine that I dare not open, unless it is full of live scorpions.

3. At an April Fools' dance, the following rules are prescribed. Any boy who breaks a rule must pay a forfeit.

(a) If a boy dances with a redhead or fails to dance with the chaperone, then he must dance with the cook and must not dance with a blonde.
(b) A boy must not dance with the chaperone and must dance with a blonde if he does not dance with the cook or if he does dance with a redhead.
(c) A boy must dance with the chaperone but not with the cook unless he dances with a redhead and not with a blonde.

Show that every boy will pay a forfeit.

4. Simplify to a single rule the following set of rules regarding dress to be worn to a certain party for married couples.

(a) If a man wears either a tie or a coat, then his wife must wear neither high heels nor a hat.
(b) If a woman wears slacks or a hat, then her husband must wear either a tie or a hat, but not both.
(c) No man and wife may both wear hats unless either the wife wears high heels and slacks or the man wears a tie and does not wear a coat.
(d) For every couple, either the man or his wife must wear a hat and either the man wear a coat or the wife wear slacks.
(e) If a man wears a hat or his wife wears slacks, then the man must wear a tie and his wife must not wear high heels.

The following two problems are not so adaptable to the methods of this section as are the preceding problems. Whereas the solutions to earlier problems can be found merely by translating given propositions into symbols and performing the necessary combinations or simplifications, in the following problems most of the implications needed in the solution are not specifically stated, but are implied by the situations described. In each problem, formalize your solution as far as possible.

5. In a certain mythical community, politicians always lie, and nonpoliticians always tell the truth. A stranger meets three natives, and asks the first of them if he is a politician. The first native answers the question. The second native then reports that the first native denied being a politician. Then the third native asserts that the first native is really a politician. How many of these natives are politicians?

6. Of three prisoners in a certain jail, one had normal vision, the second had only one eye, and the third was totally blind. All were of at least average intelligence. The jailer told the prisoners that from a selection of three white hats and two red hats, he would choose three hats and put them on the prisoners' heads. Each was prevented from seeing the color of the hat placed on his own head. The prisoners were brought together, and the jailer offered freedom to the prisoner with normal vision if he could tell the color of the hat that was on his head. The prisoner confessed that he couldn't tell. Next the jailer offered freedom to the prisoner with only one eye if he could tell the color of the hat on his head. The second prisoner confessed that he couldn't tell. The jailer did not bother making the offer to the blind prisoner, but agreed to extend the same terms to him when he made the request. The blind prisoner then smiled broadly and said,

"I do not need to have my sight;
From what my friends with eyes have said,
I can clearly see my hat is _____."

Fill in the blank correctly.

REFERENCES

ALLENDOERFER and OAKLEY, *Principles of Mathematics*, McGraw-Hill, 1955.

CARROLL, LEWIS, *Symbolic Logic*, MacMillan, 4th ed., 1955.

CHRISTIAN, R. R., *Introduction to Logic and Sets*, Ginn and Co., 1958.

COURANT and ROBBINS, *What is Mathematics?*, Oxford Press, 1941.

KEMENY, SNELL, and THOMPSON, *Introduction to Finite Mathematics*, Prentice-Hall, 1957.

LANGER, SUSANNE, *An Introduction to Symbolic Logic*, Dover Publications, 2nd ed., 1953.

ROSENBLOOM, PAUL, *The Elements of Mathematical Logic*, Dover Publications, 1950.

TARSKI, ALFRED, *Introduction to Logic*, Oxford Press, 1946.

CHAPTER 4

SWITCHING ALGEBRA

4–1 Introduction. In this chapter, we will introduce a third important application of Boolean algebra, the algebra of circuits, involving two-state (bistable) devices. The simplest example of such a device is a switch or contact. The theory introduced holds equally well for such two-state devices as rectifying diodes, magnetic cores, transistors, various types of electron tubes, etc. The nature of the two states varies with the device and includes conducting versus nonconducting, closed versus open, charged versus discharged, magnetized versus nonmagnetized, high-potential versus low-potential, and others.

The algebra of circuits is receiving more attention at present, both from mathematicians and from engineers, than either of the two applications of Boolean algebra which we considered in the previous chapters. The importance of the subject is reflected in the use of Boolean algebra in the design and simplification of complex circuits involved in electronic computers, dial telephone switching systems, and many varied kinds of electronic control devices.

The algebra of circuits fits into the general picture of Boolean algebra as an algebra with two elements 0 and 1. This means that except for the terminology and meaning connecting it with circuits, it is identical with the algebra of propositions considered as an abstract system. Either of these Boolean algebras is much more restricted than an algebra of sets. The latter concept is so general, in fact, that every Boolean algebra may be interpreted as an algebra of sets (see Section 2–6).

4–2 Definition of the algebraic symbols. For the present, we will limit our discussion to the simplest kinds of circuits, those involving only switches. We will designate a switch by a single letter $a, b, c, x, y, \ldots$ If two switches operate so that they open and close simultaneously, we designate them by the same letter. If they operate so that the first is always open when the second is closed, and closed when the second is open, we denote the first by a letter, say x, and the second by x' (or, equally well, the first by x' and the second by x).

A circuit consisting of two switches x and y connected in parallel is denoted by $x + y$, and a circuit consisting of x and y connected in series is denoted by xy. Thus to each series-parallel circuit, there corresponds an algebraic expression; and conversely to each algebraic expression

75

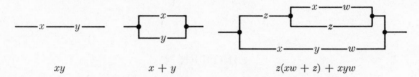

xy $\qquad\qquad\qquad x + y$ $\qquad\qquad\qquad z(xw + z) + xyw$

Fɪɢ. 4–1. Correspondence functions with circuits.

involving only $(+)$, $(\cdot)$, and $(')$, there corresponds a circuit (see Fig. 4–1). We will speak of this relationship by saying that the function *represents* the circuit, and the circuit *realizes* the function.

We will agree to assign the value 1 to a letter if it represents a closed switch, and the value 0 if it represents an open switch. If a and a' both appear, then a is 1 if and only if a' is 0. A switch that is always closed is represented by 1, one that is always open by 0. Letters play the role of variables which take on the value 0 or 1, and we note the close analogy to proposition variables, which have the same possible values, although the meaning attached to these values has changed.

Two circuits involving switches a, b, ... are said to be *equivalent* if the closure conditions of the two circuits are the same for any given position of the switches involved (values of the variables a, b, ...). That is, they are equivalent if for every position of the switches, current may either pass through both (both closed) or not pass through either (both open). Two algebraic expressions are defined to be *equal* if and only if they represent equivalent circuits.

From these definitions, it should be clear that the only circuit properties of interest in the algebra of circuits are closure properties. That is, we will investigate only those factors which determine whether a circuit is open or closed, and will not be interested in problems concerning the resistance, amount of current or voltage, etc. It will be enough to know whether the circuit will carry a current, and we will ignore all quantitative considerations. This situation is an exact analogy of the situation in logic, where Boolean algebra was found capable of handling only that part of logic dependent on the truth values of propositions. Shades of meaning, and all considerations other than truth values, are beyond the reach of algebraic techniques.

It is now possible, by drawing the appropriate circuits and enumerating the possible positions of the switches involved, to check that each of the laws of Boolean algebra is valid when interpreted in terms of switching

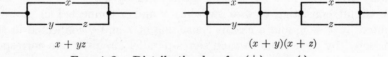

$x + yz$ $\qquad\qquad\qquad\qquad\qquad (x + y)(x + z)$

Fɪɢ. 4–2. Distributive law for $(+)$ over $(\cdot)$.

TABLE 4–1

CLOSURE PROPERTIES OF SWITCHING FUNCTIONS a', ab, AND $a + b$

Row	a	b	a'	ab	$a + b$
1	1	1	0	1	1
2	1	0	0	0	1
3	0	1	1	0	1
4	0	0	1	0	0

circuits. For example, consider the circuits that realize the functions on each side of the identity stating the distributive law for $(+)$ over $(\cdot)$, shown in Fig. 4–2. By inspection, it is apparent that the circuit is closed (current can pass) if switch x is closed, or if both y and z are closed, and that the circuit is open (current cannot pass) if x and either y or z are open. Hence the circuits are equivalent, and this distributive law holds.

A simpler procedure for checking the validity of the fundamental laws is to note that numerical values of the switching functions a', ab, and $a + b$ are identical to the truth tables for the corresponding propositional functions (Table 4–1). Hence the verification by truth tables of the postulates of Boolean algebra given in Chapter 3 is also a proof that the algebra of circuits is a Boolean algebra. The student should write out these proofs as a review.

EXAMPLE 1. Find a circuit which realizes the Boolean function $xyz' + x'(y + z')$.

Solution. This expression indicates a series connection of x, y, and z' in parallel with a circuit corresponding to $x'(y + z')$. This latter circuit consists of x' in series with a parallel connection of y and z'. Hence the circuit diagram is that shown in Fig. 4–3.

EXAMPLE 2. Find the Boolean function which represents the circuit shown in Fig. 4–4.

Solution. By inspection, the function is $(x + y' + z)uv(yz' + x + y'u)$.

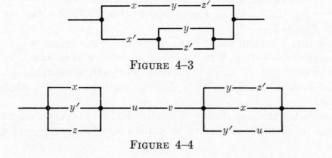

FIGURE 4–3

FIGURE 4–4

EXAMPLE 3. Construct the table of closure properties for the function $f = x'y + z(x + y')$.

Solution. A table of closure properties for a function is identical, except for interpretation, to a truth table for a propositional function. This function has the closure properties listed in Table 4–2.

TABLE 4–2

CLOSURE PROPERTIES FOR THE FUNCTION $f = x'y + z(x + y')$

Row	x	y	z	$x'y$	$x + y'$	$z(x + y')$	$x'y + z(x + y')$
1	1	1	1	0	1	1	1
2	1	1	0	0	1	0	0
3	1	0	1	0	1	1	1
4	1	0	0	0	1	0	0
5	0	1	1	1	0	0	1
6	0	1	0	1	0	0	1
7	0	0	1	0	1	1	1
8	0	0	0	0	1	0	0

EXERCISES

1. Draw the circuits indicated by the two laws of absorption and the distributive law for (·) over (+), and check the validity of the laws by showing that the circuits are equivalent.

2. Draw circuits which realize each of the following expressions, without first simplifying the expressions.

(a) $abc + ab(dc + ef)$
(b) $a + b(c + de) + fg$
(c) $x[y(z + w) + z(u + v)]$
(d) $(a + b' + c)(a + bc') + c'd + d(b' + c)$

3. Find the function which represents each of the circuits in Fig. 4–5.

4. (a) Find a circuit which is closed when the circuit of Fig. 4–5(a) is open, and open when the circuit of Fig. 4–5(a) is closed. (b) Do the same for the circuit of Fig. 4–5(d).

5. Show that if we had used (+) to represent a series connection, (·) to represent a parallel connection, 0 to represent a closed switch, and 1 to represent an open switch, and all other definitions were left unchanged, the resulting algebra of circuits would also be a Boolean algebra. (Some authors use this notation.)

6. Construct a table of closure properties for the function in Exercise 2(d).

7. Construct a table of closure properties for the circuits of Figs. 4–5(b) and (d).

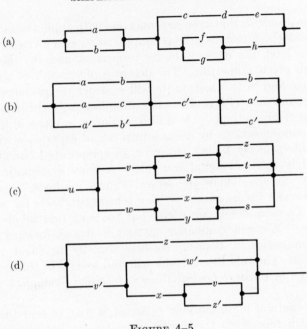

FIGURE 4-5

8. Find circuits which realize each of the functions given in Table 4-3. [*Hint:* First construct the functions exactly according to the method given in Section 2-4 or in Section 2-5, and then draw the circuits which realize each function.]

TABLE 4-3

Row	x	y	z	f_1	f_2	f_3	f_4
1	1	1	1	0	1	1	1
2	1	1	0	1	0	1	1
3	1	0	1	1	0	0	0
4	1	0	0	0	1	1	1
5	0	1	1	0	1	1	1
6	0	1	0	0	1	0	0
7	0	0	1	0	0	1	0
8	0	0	0	1	1	1	0

4-3 Simplification of circuits. In the previous section, we showed that the algebra of circuits is a Boolean algebra, and hence all the results proved earlier for Boolean algebras hold. In particular, theorems and rules relating to simplification of Boolean functions apply in the algebra of circuits.

Two basic problems that arise in connection with applications of Boolean algebra to switching circuits are (a) simplification of a given circuit which is known to have the desired closure properties, and (b) the design of circuits with given properties. The design problem will be discussed in later sections, and in this section we will consider the problem of simplifying a given circuit. This problem has often been solved in specific cases by trial-and-error methods. A skilled engineer is often able to make remarkable simplifications by using intuition and experience with similar circuits as his primary tools. However, in complicated circuits such as those found in modern digital computers, a more systematic approach is extremely useful. There are several known methods, based on the theory of Boolean functions, for writing schematic charts for simplifying functions. These methods are useful but too long and involved for inclusion here. We will emphasize instead a straightforward approach using the properties of Boolean algebras directly to effect reasonable simplifications. The interested reader will find several of the more formal methods given in Phister, *Logical Design of Digital Computers*, and other sources.

A general method of simplifying a circuit is first to find the Boolean function which represents the circuit, then to simplify the function as we have done repeatedly in earlier sections, and finally to draw a new circuit diagram realizing the simplified function.

EXAMPLE 1. Simplify the circuit in Fig. 4–6(a).

Solution. This circuit is represented by the Boolean function

$$(xy + abc)(xy + a' + b' + c'),$$

which simplifies to xy. Hence the given circuit is equivalent to the series connection of the two switches x and y, with the diagram given in Fig. 4–6(b).

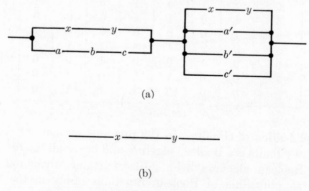

(a)

(b)

FIGURE 4–6

Two problems inherent in any simplification procedure should be mentioned at the outset. First, it may be difficult, or impossible, to tell from the Boolean function alone which of several circuits is "simplest." The best circuit may well depend on the relative cost of wiring and of various types of switches required by the several equal functions which may be written. The final simplification, then, depends upon the specifications for a given circuit.

Another difficulty is that the simplest, or most economical, circuit may not be a series-parallel circuit. Since Boolean algebra reflects this type of circuit only, the final simplification may often be performed by the designer who recognizes such a possibility. In this step, Boolean algebra is of no help. Two kinds of circuits in which the series-parallel circuit is not the best form are discussed in later sections. For the time being, we will omit any such considerations.

In using the basic laws of Boolean algebra, it often happens that a possible simplification is overlooked. It may happen that a certain step is easier to recognize if stated in terms of one of the dual laws rather than in terms of the other. This suggests another method of simplification which may help. To simplify a function f, the dual of f may be taken and the resulting expression simplified. If the dual is taken again, the function f is obtained in a different form. This will usually be simpler than the original.

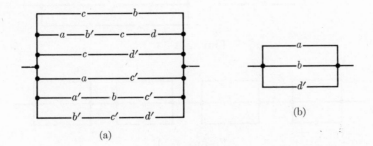

(a)   (b)

FIGURE 4–7

EXAMPLE 2. Simplify the circuit in Fig. 4–7(a).

Solution. The circuit is represented by the function

$$f = cb + ab'cd + cd' + ac' + a'bc' + b'c'd'.$$

Consider the first three terms as the function g, and the last three terms as the function h. Then

$$g = cb + ab'cd + cd'.$$

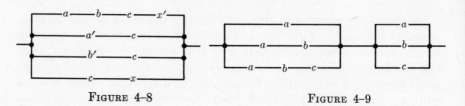

FIGURE 4–8   FIGURE 4–9

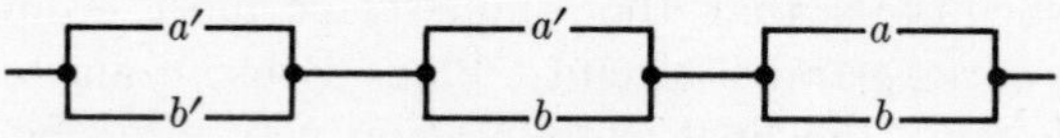

FIGURE 4–10

FIGURE 4–11   FIGURE 4–12

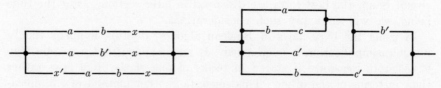

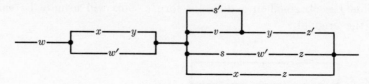

FIGURE 4–13

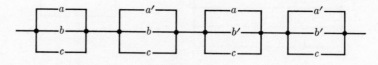

FIGURE 4–14

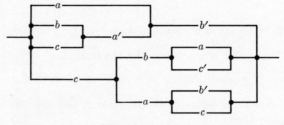

FIGURE 4–15

The dual of g, which we will write $d(g)$, is then

$$d(g) = (c + b)(a + b' + c + d)(c + d') = c + abd'.$$

Taking the dual again, we find

$$g = c(a + b + d').$$

Similarly,

$$h = ac' + a'bc' + b'c'd',$$
$$d(h) = (a + c')(a' + b + c')(b' + c' + d') = c' + abd',$$
$$h = c'(a + b + d').$$

Combining g and h yields

$$f = (c + c')(a + b + d') = a + b + d',$$

which corresponds to the circuit in Fig. 4–7(b).

EXERCISES

1–8. Simplify the circuits in Figs. 4–8 through 4–15.

4–4 Non-series-parallel circuits. It has been shown that every series-parallel circuit corresponds to a Boolean function and conversely that every Boolean function corresponds to a series-parallel circuit. Boolean functions can also be found which reflect the properties, although not the geometry, of other types of circuits. We will present three methods of writing a Boolean function for such circuits. The converse of this problem, that of finding a *non-series-parallel circuit* for a given function, will be discussed only partially. In fact, no general solution is known except in the special case of symmetric circuits, which will be treated in a later section.

So far we have discussed 2-terminal circuits only. One may think of such a circuit as being designed to control the operation of a light connected in series with a battery and the given circuit. Changes made in simplification are such that the set of positions which will cause the light to shine are not altered. Such changes correspond to exactly those simplifications of the associated function allowable within a Boolean algebra.

We must introduce the concept of an *n-terminal circuit*. Fig. 4–16 shows a 3-terminal circuit. This circuit is simply a combination of three

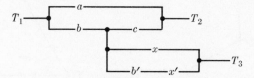

FIG. 4–16. A 3-terminal circuit.

2-terminal circuits. We may think of this circuit as controlling a light by any of the three circuits joining points labelled T_1, T_2, and T_3. We may designate the various functions as follows: f_{12} will denote the 2-terminal circuit joining T_1 to T_2; f_{13} that joining T_1 to T_3; and f_{23} that joining T_2 to T_3. We could, of course, visualize this circuit as simultaneously controlling the operations of three light bulbs, each with different operating characteristics in terms of the positions of the switches involved.

In general, an n-terminal circuit will be defined as a configuration of switches connected by wires in which n points are designated as terminals. The $\frac{1}{2}n(n - 1)$ possible functions are designated f_{ij}, denoting the function corresponding to the 2-terminal circuit joining T_i to T_j for each i and j, where $i \neq j$; but otherwise i and j may assume any pair of values from 1 to n inclusive. Two such circuits are equivalent if each pair of 2-terminal circuits are equivalent or, as well, if the functions representing the pairs of corresponding circuits are equal.

As in ordinary circuit theory, there exist *wye-to-delta* and *delta-to-wye transformations*. We introduce these transformations to develop a method for reducing a non-series-parallel circuit to an equivalent circuit of series-parallel type. (The method actually depends only on the wye-to-delta transformation. The other is included only as a matter of interest.) We shall define a *wye circuit* as a 3-terminal circuit, where the three 2-terminal circuits involved have a common point other than a terminal. A *delta circuit* is a 3-terminal circuit in which the only common points of any pair of the three 2-terminal circuits are the three terminals, each of which is common to exactly two of the 2-terminal circuits.

The wye-to-delta transformation is shown in Fig. 4–17. That the wye-to-delta transformation gives an equivalent circuit is immediately apparent from noting that the 2-terminal circuits formed in each case are series connections of the same pairs of switches.

The delta-to-wye transformation is shown in Fig. 4–18. That the delta-to-wye transformation gives an equivalent circuit follows from the distributive law for $(+)$ over $(\cdot)$. For example, $f_{12} = x + zy = (x + z)(x + y)$,

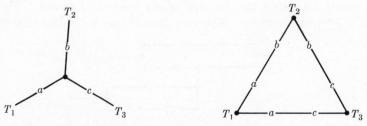

FIG. 4–17. Wye-to-delta transformation.

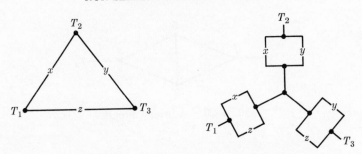

FIG. 4–18. Delta-to-wye transformation.

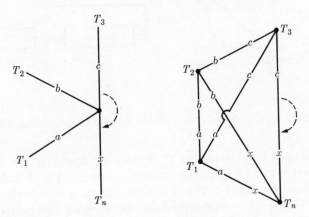

FIG. 4–19. Star-to-mesh transformation.

where the first form represents the delta circuit, and the second represents the wye circuit.

The wye-to-delta transformation may be generalized to a *star-to-mesh transformation*, where the star represents an n-terminal circuit with a common central point which is eliminated to give an equivalent mesh circuit. Figure 4–19 suggests the method employed. That this transformation produces an equivalent circuit is self-evident, although a formal proof by induction may be given. It can also be shown that if the original circuit contains a single n-point star but no m-point star, for $m > n$, the new circuit will contain no star with more than $n - 1$ points. Hence, a systematic reduction is possible, leading to a circuit with no stars at all, that is, a series-parallel circuit.

As an application of the wye-to-delta transformation, consider the problem of finding a Boolean function to represent the bridge circuit of Fig. 4–20, a non-series-parallel circuit. The vertices of the circuit are labelled with capital letters for reference. The point Q is the central point

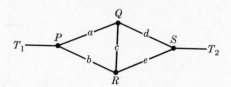

FIG. 4–20. A bridge circuit.

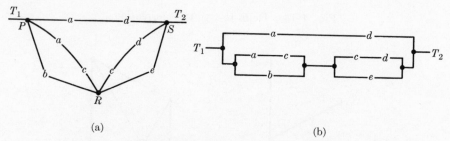

(a)   (b)

FIG. 4–21. Transformed circuit for the bridge of Fig. 4–20.

of a wye circuit with terminals P, R, and S. Applying the wye-to-delta transformation gives an equivalent circuit shown in Fig. 4–21(a), redrawn for convenience in Fig. 4–21(b). From this figure, it follows that the bridge circuit of Fig. 4–20 is represented by the Boolean function $f_{12} = ad + (ac + b)(cd + e)$, even though the function does not suggest the geometry of the given circuit. Conversely, we may say that if any function corresponds exactly to f in form, it is possible to use a bridge circuit to represent the function. It is obvious that to identify a combination of this type in a given Boolean function is not easy.

The method presented in the preceding paragraph generalizes with the use of the star-to-mesh transformations to find a method for obtaining a Boolean function for any given circuit, series-parallel or not, and for complicated circuits is probably better than either of the following methods.

Two alternative methods of obtaining the Boolean function for a circuit are easier to use in simple cases, but have the disadvantage of being essentially trial-and-error methods and hence subject to error in complicated cases. The first of these consists of examining the circuit for all possible combinations of closed switches which allow a current through the circuit. Broken lines in Fig. 4–22 illustrate this method. These paths for the bridge circuit correspond to the combinations ad, be, ace, and bcd. The function f_{12} may then be written as $f_{12} = ad + be + ace + bcd$, which is clearly equal to the function obtained previously.

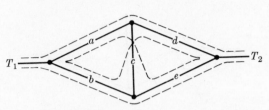

FIG. 4–22. Possible paths in a bridge circuit.

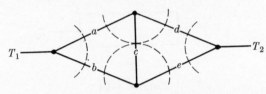

FIG. 4–23. Possible breaks in a bridge circuit.

The second alternative method (the third method to be considered) is illustrated in Fig. 4–23. In this method, broken lines through the circuit are drawn in all possible ways in which the circuit may be broken (by a combination of open switches). These combinations are a, b; d, e; a, c, e; and b, c, d. An alternative form for the function is then given by $f_{12} = (a + b)(d + e)(a + c + e)(b + c + d)$, which has the value 0 if any of the four sets of switches is open. This form is easily shown to be equal to the two previous forms for f_{12}.

Any of these three methods can be made a basis for the problem of determining whether a function f can be realized by a non-series-parallel circuit. For such a method, one would first examine the properties of various types of such circuits, for example the bridge of Fig. 4–20. These properties could be given in a table or by a special form for the corresponding function. Then the given Boolean function could be compared for possible similarity with the bridge function or table. (See Example 2 below.) Such a method is difficult to apply, but Boolean functions are not well-adapted to more direct methods, since the operations refer directly only to series-parallel circuits.

It should be mentioned that even where a bridge circuit exists, it is not always simpler than an equivalent series-parallel circuit. (See Example 1 below.) In some cases, then, searching for a bridge circuit may be a waste of time.

EXAMPLE 1. Simplify the circuit in Fig. 4–24(a).

Solution. Using method 3,

$$f_{12} = (x'y + x + z)(x + z)(x'y + y + z)(x + z + y + x) = xy + z,$$

and the circuit is therefore equivalent to the circuit in Fig. 4–24(b).

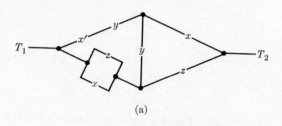

(a)

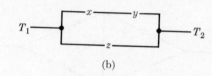

(b)

FIGURE 4–24

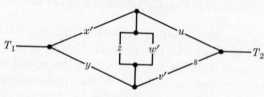

FIGURE 4–25

EXAMPLE 2. Draw a bridge circuit for the function

$$f = (x'u + x'v's + yu + yv's)(x' + z + w' + v's)(y + z + w' + u).$$

Solution. Expanding f, we find by comparison with method 2 that we can write f as

$$f = x'u + yv's + x'(z + w')v's + y(z + w')u.$$

Hence, f is realized by the bridge of Fig. 4–20 if we let $a = x'$, $b = y$, $c = z + w'$, $d = u$, and $e = v's$. The circuit is shown in Fig. 4–25.

EXERCISES

1. Use method 3 to find the Boolean function which represents the circuit in Fig. 4–26. Simplify if possible.

2. Use method 2 to find the Boolean function which represents the circuit in Fig. 4–27. Simplify if possible.

3. Use method 1 to find the Boolean function which represents the circuit in Fig. 4–28. Simplify if possible.

4. Find, and simplify if possible, a Boolean function representing each of the circuits in Fig. 4–29.

5. Construct a bridge circuit which realizes the function

$$f = xw' + y'uv + (xz + y')(zw' + uv).$$

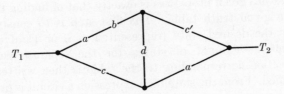

FIGURE 4–26

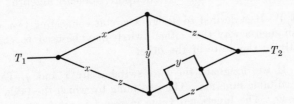

FIGURE 4–27

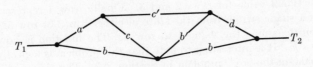

FIGURE 4–28

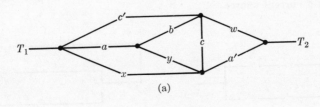

(a)

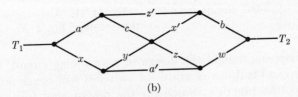

(b)

FIGURE 4–29

4–5 Design of circuits from given properties. The problem of designing a circuit that has given properties is exactly that of finding the proposition which has a given truth table. The first step is to construct the table which gives the desired state (represented as 0 or 1) of the circuit for each possible assignment of states for the separate switches. The Boolean function corresponding to the table is then written and, if possible, simplified. From the simplified expression a circuit is drawn. Further simplifications may be possible by using non-series-parallel circuits such as the bridge in Section 4–4, but here the problem depends more upon the ingenuity of the designer than upon Boolean algebra.

EXAMPLE 1. It is desired to design a circuit connecting two switches and a light bulb in such a way that either switch may be used to control the light independently of the state of the other.

Solution. If we designate the two switches by x and y, Table 4–4 corresponds to a suitable function. The reasoning by which the table is constructed goes as follows. The functional value in row 1 is arbitrary if we do not care whether the light is on or off for any given position of the switches. If we assign the value 1, then either row 2 or row 3 represents a change of state of a single switch, and this is required to change the state of the light. Hence, 0 is the proper functional value for rows 2 and 3. Finally, row 4 represents a change of state of a single switch from the state of either row 2 or row 3. Hence, the function must assume the value 1 in row 4. The function is now written as $f = xy + x'y'$. It is interesting to note that this problem is logically equivalent to the "snake-in-the-box" problem in Section 3–3. The circuit may be drawn as in Fig. 4–30. However, the diagram of Fig. 4–31 is perhaps more suggestive of the actual wiring that is required. The switch pairs (x, x') and (y, y') each consists of a single-pole double-throw switch. The symbol $\dashv\vdash$ is the usual one indicating a current source.

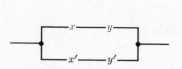

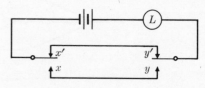

FIG. 4–30. Control circuit for a 2-way light switch.

FIG. 4–31. Alternative diagram for the circuit of Fig. 4–30.

It often happens that in the design of a switching circuit, it is known that certain combinations of states of switches will never occur. When this happens, the function chosen for the design may take on either of the values 0 or 1 for such combinations without affecting the results. We will represent such combinations by placing the symbol (?) in the function column of the table of closure properties. A suitable choice of values

TABLE 4–4

Row	x	y	f
1	1	1	1
2	1	0	0
3	0	1	0
4	0	0	1

TABLE 4–5

Row	x	y	z	w	f
1	1	1	0	1	1
2	1	1	0	0	1
3	1	0	0	1	1
4	1	0	0	0	1

corresponding to the rows marked with (?) may greatly simplify the resulting circuit. A formal set of rules could be stated which would completely solve this problem, but we will give just two rules which are often of considerable help.

RULE 1. If it is possible to assign all 0's or all 1's and thereby leave a small number of rows having value 1 (or 0) while all others have the complementary value, then a correspondingly simple disjunctive normal form (or conjunctive normal form) will give the function.

RULE 2. It may be possible to assign 0's and 1's in a fashion to make the function independent of one or more letters, thereby simplifying the resulting circuit.

The application of Rule 1 is obvious. In applying Rule 2, we will think entirely in terms of writing the function in disjunctive normal form. If this form contains two terms alike except for one variable, then that variable may be eliminated. For example $xyz' + xyz = xy(z + z') = xy$. This corresponds to saying that if two rows of the table for which the function takes the value 1 are alike except for the state of a single switch, then the two rows can be represented by a single term independent of the variable representing that switch. Similarly, if four rows for which the function takes the value 1 are alike except for the states of two switches, then the four rows can be represented by a single term independent of the two variables corresponding to these switches. The reason for this is that the columns corresponding to like states will be represented by common factors in the disjunctive normal form, and the remaining variables will appear only in a factor which is the complete disjunctive normal form in these variables and hence may be deleted. Consider the four rows of Table 4–5, for instance. Representing the rows directly, we obtain

$$xyz'w + xyz'w' + xy'z'w + xy'z'w' = xz'(yw + yw' + y'w + y'w') = xz'.$$

This simplification can be performed by inspection, thus avoiding the necessity of writing the longer expression. The method can be extended to the case where 2^n rows are alike except for the states of n switches, but it becomes increasingly more difficult to isolate such possibilities by the inspection of a table. This method, of course, applies also in cases where no ? appears in any row whenever like rows are present.

A final help in constructing a function for a given table comes from noting that if any letter, say x, has the value 1 in every row for which the function is 1, then x is a factor of the function. Similarly, if every row shows the value 0 for x, then x' is a factor of the function.

EXAMPLE 2. Design a circuit having the properties given in Table 4–6.

TABLE 4–6

Row	x	y	z	$g(x, y, z)$
1	1	1	1	1
2	1	1	0	0
3	1	0	1	0
4	1	0	0	0
5	0	1	1	?
6	0	1	0	?
7	0	0	1	0
8	0	0	0	?

Solution 1. Using Rule 1 and noting that only a single 1 appears in the function column, if we assign 0 to each ? the function $f = xyz$ will result. The circuit is a series connection of switches x, y, and z.

Solution 2. If we use Rule 2 and note that if we assign 1 to row 5 and 0 to each of rows 6 and 8, the function becomes independent of x and may be written as $f = yz$. The circuit is now a series connection of y and z only, which is simpler than the circuit of Solution 1. Of course, the two circuits are not equivalent, but they differ only in the cases that do not arise, and hence either will serve.

It is unnecessary to list an entire table of closure properties. It is sufficient merely to list those rows for which the function is 1, assuming that all unlisted rows correspond to combinations for which the function is to be 0. This practice will be adopted in the future wherever it is convenient.

EXERCISES

1. Design series-parallel circuits as simply as possible with properties given by each of the columns headed f, g, h, and k in Table 4–7.

TABLE 4–7

Row	x	y	z	f	g	h	k
1	1	1	1	1	1	0	0
2	1	1	0	0	0	1	0
3	1	0	1	0	1	1	1
4	1	0	0	1	1	0	?
5	0	1	1	0	0	?	1
6	0	1	0	1	0	0	1
7	0	0	1	0	1	?	?
8	0	0	0	0	1	1	?

2. Table 4–8 lists the combinations for which a circuit is to be closed. For all other positions of u, v, x, y, and z, the circuit is to be open. Design the simplest series-parallel circuit with these properties.

TABLE 4–8

Row	u	v	x	y	z
1	1	0	1	1	1
2	0	0	1	1	1
3	1	0	1	0	1
4	0	0	0	1	1
5	1	0	0	1	1
6	1	0	0	0	1

3. Two alternately operating projectors are used to show continuous movies. Suppose that each projector is provided with a switch and that it is desired to wire the switches with the projectors so that either switch may be used independently of the other to change from one projector to the other. Design the circuit.

4. Switches x and y independently control the pump forcing oil into a furnace. A third switch z is controlled by a thermocouple in such a way as to close automatically when the pilot light goes out. Design a circuit for the switches x, y, and z so that either switch x or y will change the state of the pump from off to on or from on to off, except that when the pilot light is out the pump will never be on.

5. Design as simply as possible a series-parallel circuit for the operation of a light independently from three switches x, y, and z. Can you simplify this circuit further by using a non-series-parallel circuit?

6. All guests are required to wear green to a certain St. Patrick's Day party. However, the green is limited to green sox, green tie, green shirt, or a green ribbon, and controlled by the following rules.

(a) A green shirt must be worn if a green tie is worn.

(b) Green sox and a green shirt may be worn together only if either a green tie or a green ribbon is also worn.

(c) If either a green shirt and a green ribbon are worn or green sox are not worn, then a green tie must be worn.

The penalty for breaking a rule is the paying of a forfeit. A judge is posted at the door to check on whether each guest must pay a forfeit. To help make rapid decisions, he would like a simple electric "brain" to help him check. The device is to have a red and a green light and four switches corresponding to tie, shirt, sox, and ribbon, which he will adjust according to the costume a guest wears. Design a circuit for each light so that the red light will shine when a forfeit must be paid and the green light will shine if all is well. [*Hint:* First combine and simplify the given rules.]

4–6 Design of n-terminal circuits. A general n-terminal circuit was defined in Section 4–4. In this section, we will consider the problem of designing certain special types of n-terminal circuits, where the design problem can be treated as the problem of combining a set of specified 2-terminal circuits into an n-terminal circuit in such a way as to share switches or parts of circuits so far as possible. To illustrate the possibilities, consider the two functions $f = a(x + y)$ and $g = axy$. The separate circuits and a combined circuit are shown in Fig. 4–32. It is apparent that the combined circuit can be used to obtain either function f or function g and with one less switch than the two circuits require if drawn separately. In addition, a new function, f_{24}, has been introduced (representing the circuit joining terminals T_2 and T_4). Provided that the possibility of a closed circuit between T_2 and T_4 does not create other problems in connection with the apparatus being designed, the 3-terminal circuit may be used in place of the two 2-terminal circuits with a saving in the number of switches needed. This illustration leads to the following definition of the problem we will consider.

We assume given a set $f_1, f_2, \ldots, f_n$ of functions (or a statement of properties leading to such functions), where some or all of the switches involved are common to more than one function. We will design an

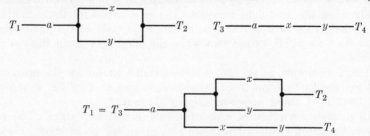

Fig. 4–32. Two 2-terminal circuits and a combined circuit.

$(n + 1)$-terminal circuit with terminals $T_0, T_1, \ldots, T_n$, where the function f_i represents the circuit connecting T_0 to T_i for each $i = 1, 2, \ldots, n$. We will assume that the possible closed paths between T_i and T_j, $i \neq 0$, $j \neq 0$, will cause no complications in the application of the circuit, and we will ignore the functions representing all such circuits.

This problem is, of course, a severe simplification of the more general problem of design in which each of the possible circuits is to have specified properties. The problem is still sufficiently general to have considerable value, and has the advantage of being easy to solve. In fact, the problem consists solely of examining the functions for common factors. Any such factors indicate portions of the circuits which may be shared.

If the functions involved are given explicitly, one may factor by trial and error in the attempt to find common factors, or each function may be placed in conjunctive normal form, from which common factors may be determined by inspection.

EXAMPLE 1. Design a 4-terminal circuit to realize the following three functions, using common switches wherever possible:

$$f = xy'z + (xy' + x'y)zw,$$
$$g = xy'zw' + x'yzw',$$
$$h = x'y + (xy' + x'y)(z' + w').$$

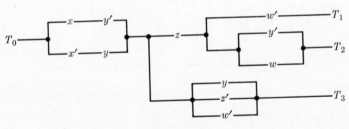

FIGURE 4–33

Solution. Since g can be most easily factored, we begin by writing it in the form

$$g = (xy' + x'y)zw'.$$

Examining f and h for possible factors in common with g, we find

$$\begin{aligned}
f &= z[xy' + (xy' + x'y)w] \\
&= z[xy'y' + x'yy' + (xy' + x'y)w] \\
&= z[(xy' + x'y)y' + (xy' + x'y)w] \\
&= (xy' + x'y)z(y' + w).
\end{aligned}$$

Similarly,

$$h = x'y + (xy' + x'y)(z' + w')$$
$$= x'yy + xy'y + (xy' + x'y)(z' + w')$$
$$= (x'y + xy')y + (xy' + x'y)(z' + w')$$
$$= (xy' + x'y)(y + z' + w').$$

Hence the required circuit is that of Fig. 4–33, where $f = f_{02}$, $g = f_{01}$, and $h = f_{03}$.

If the functions are not given, but the properties are specified by a table as in Section 4–5, the best procedure is to first write each function in conjunctive normal form. Common factors may be found either from the table or from the functions. The circuit is then drawn in such a way as to make the best possible use of common factors.

EXAMPLE 2. Construct a 4-terminal circuit to realize the functions f, g, and h, with properties given by Table 4–9.

TABLE 4–9

Row	x	y	z	f	g	h
1	1	1	1	1	0	0
2	1	1	0	0	1	1
3	1	0	1	1	1	1
4	1	0	0	0	0	0
5	0	1	1	1	0	0
6	0	1	0	0	1	1
7	0	0	1	1	0	1
8	0	0	0	1	0	1

Solution. First, each function is written in conjunctive normal form:

$$f = (x' + y + z)(x' + y' + z)(x + y' + z),$$
$$g = (x' + y + z)(x' + y' + z')(x + y' + z')(x + y + z)(x + y + z'),$$
$$h = (x' + y + z)(x' + y' + z')(x + y' + z').$$

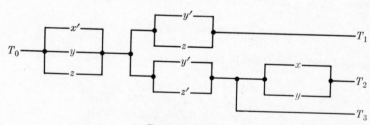

FIGURE 4–34

The common factors are noted and are indicated below with vertical lines. Simplifications are made where possible.

$$f = (x' + y + z) \mid (y' + z)$$
$$g = (x' + y + z) \mid (y' + z') \mid (x + y).$$
$$h = (x' + y + z) \mid (y' + z')$$

The final circuit is shown in Fig. 4–34, where $f = f_{01}$, $g = f_{02}$, and $h = f_{03}$.

In addition to cases in which the functions have common factors, there are certain other cases in which sharing of switches is possible. These cases will be easier to discuss in connection with the use of special types of switches called *transfer contacts*. We will postpone this discussion until the next chapter.

EXERCISES

1. Construct a 3-terminal circuit to realize both of the following functions:

$$f = xzw + y'zw,$$
$$g = xzw + y'zw + x'y'z.$$

2. Construct a 4-terminal circuit to realize all three of the functions specified by Table 4–10. Share switches where possible.

TABLE 4–10

Row	x	y	z	f	g	h
1	1	1	1	0	0	0
2	1	1	0	1	1	1
3	1	0	1	1	0	0
4	1	0	0	0	1	0
5	0	1	1	0	0	0
6	0	1	0	1	1	1
7	0	0	1	1	1	0
8	0	0	0	0	1	0

3. Construct a 4-terminal circuit to realize the following three functions, sharing switches where possible:

$$f = a(b + cd)(x + y),$$
$$g = a(bc + cd),$$
$$h = a(bc' + b'cd).$$

Ten switches are sufficient for this diagram.

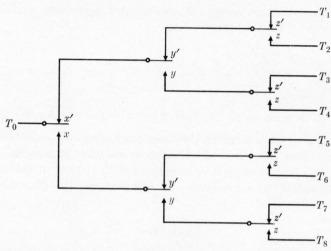

FIGURE 4-35

4. The diagram in Fig. 4–35, sometimes called a *complete transfer tree*, is sufficient to realize any function of three variables by joining appropriate terminals T_i to a common lead. Each symbol $-\!\!\circ\!\!\begin{smallmatrix} x' \\ x \end{smallmatrix}$ is called a *transfer contact* and corresponds to a single-pole double-throw switch.

(a) Show that each function f_{0i} realizes exactly one row of the closure table for three switches (or, equivalently, one of the eight logical possibilities for three variables).

(b) Use the transfer tree to construct the circuit which realizes the function $f = xy + y'z$. [*Hint:* First put f in disjunctive normal form.]

(c) Use the transfer tree to construct a circuit which is closed if and only if exactly two of the switches x, y, and z are closed.

5. (a) Construct a complete transfer tree for four switches x, y, z, and w. (b) Use the transfer tree of (a) to design a 3-terminal circuit realizing the following two functions:

$$f = xyzw' + xyz'w,$$
$$g = xyzw + xyz'w'.$$

(c) Use the transfer tree of (a) to design a circuit which is closed if and only if any one or any three of the switches x, y, z, and w are closed.

6. Three students, A, B, and C, match coins each day for coffee. They flip repeatedly until one man's coin turns up unlike both other coins, whereupon this man buys the coffee. Instead of flipping coins, they decide to build a machine on which each man either opens or closes a switch, and again the odd man is to buy the coffee. Design a suitable 5-terminal circuit which will light a green light if all men are alike (indicating another try is needed), a red light if A is odd man, a blue light if B is odd man, and a yellow light if C is odd man.

4-7 Symmetric functions and their circuits. In Section 4-4, the problem of determining a Boolean function to represent a non-series-parallel circuit was discussed, and it was pointed out that it is difficult to design such a circuit to represent a given function. The general solution to this problem is not known. However, there are certain types of functions, called *symmetric functions,* for which the solution is known. The purpose of this section is to show how the most economical circuits for such functions can be constructed.

We will say that a function of n variables $x_1, x_2, \ldots, x_n$ is *symmetric* in these variables if and only if the interchange of any pair of variables leaves the function identically the same.

As examples, the function $xy' + x'y$ is symmetric in x and y, the function $xyz + x'y'z'$ is symmetric in x, y, and z, and $xy'z + x'yz + x'y'z'$ is symmetric in x, y, and z'. In addition to the many symmetric functions that arise, it is often possible to write a function in such a way that a factor, or a summand, of the function is symmetric. In these cases, the symmetric part of the function may be realized by the type of circuit discussed in this section and then combined in series or parallel with the remainder of the function.

The following theorem gives the basis for the method of design of circuits for symmetric functions.

THEOREM. A necessary and sufficient condition that a function of n variables be symmetric is that it may be specified by stating a set of numbers $n_1, n_2, \ldots, n_k$, $0 \le n_i \le n$ for each i, such that if any set of exactly n_i, $i = 1, 2, \ldots, k$, of the variables are 1, the function has the value 1 and not otherwise.

Proof. If the function is symmetric, then interchanging the variables does not change the function, hence the number of variables taking the value 1 determines the function rather than any specific assignment of 1's among the variables. Conversely, if the number of variables which have the value 1 is sufficient to determine the value of the function, the variables may be interchanged without altering the function, and hence the function is symmetric.

We will call the set of numbers $n_1, n_2, \ldots, n_k$ associated with a symmetric function the *characteristic numbers* for the function. The symmetric function $xy + xz + yz$ has characteristic numbers 2 and 3 since if either two or three of the variables are 1, the function has the value 1. Similarly, $xy' + x'y$ has the single characteristic number 1. To find the characteristic numbers for a symmetric function, it is necessary only to evaluate the function with $0, 1, \ldots, n$ of its variables as 1, and the rest as 0, in any single order and record those numbers for which the function is 1.

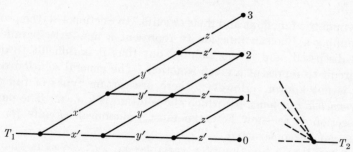

FIG. 4-36. Circuit for symmetric functions of three variables.

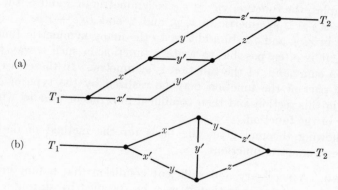

FIG. 4-37. Symmetric circuit of x, y, and z, with 2 as the characteristic number.

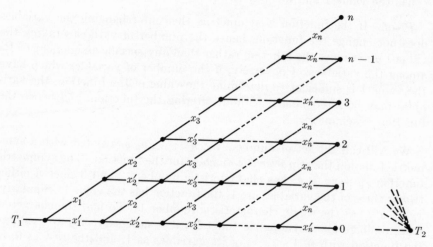

FIG. 4-38. General circuit for symmetric functions of n variables.

It can be shown that the product of two symmetric functions in the same variables is symmetric and has for its characteristic numbers those numbers common to both functions. The sum of two symmetric functions in the same variables is symmetric and has for its characteristic numbers all characteristic numbers of either or both summands. Finally, the negative (or complement) of a symmetric function in n variables is symmetric and has for its characteristic numbers all numbers from 0 to n inclusive except those which are characteristic numbers of the given function.

Before considering the general symmetric function of n variables, we will first discuss the case of three variables. Figure 4–36 shows a circuit capable of realizing any symmetric function of three variables. The levels on the right, numbered 0, 1, 2, and 3, correspond to characteristic numbers. A closed circuit between T_1 and position 2, for instance, results if and only if any two of the switches are closed.

Hence, to realize a symmetric function of three variables with characteristic numbers n_1, n_2, . . . , n_k, we connect levels n_1, n_2, . . . , n_k each to T_2 and then delete any portions of the circuit not used. For example, the function $xyz' + xy'z + x'yz$ is symmetric and has characteristic number 2. Beginning with the diagram of Fig. 4–36 and omitting unused portions, we obtain the circuit of Fig. 4–37(a), redrawn in Fig. 4–37(b), to show the bridge circuit of Section 4–4.

From this illustration, it should be reasonably clear that the diagram in Fig. 4–38 will realize any symmetric function of n variables. Levels associated with each characteristic number are connected to the terminal T_2. The resulting non-series-parallel circuit will in general be more economical of switches than a series-parallel circuit, although there are some exceptions (see Exercise 1 at the end of this section). Further simplification is possible in certain special cases.

If it happens that some relation holds between the characteristic numbers for a symmetric function, it may be possible to effect further simplifications. We will illustrate the possibilities by an example of the symmetric function in x, y, z, u, v, and w which has characteristic numbers 1, 3, and 5 (numbers in arithmetic progression). We begin with the circuit of Fig. 4–39, formed as described above, and label certain vertices for reference. Since the requirement is that the circuit be closed when an odd number of switches is closed, each closed path may be thought of as being obtained by tracing any path through the circuit in which the tracing pencil rises by one level an odd number of times. Since each level is identical to that part of every level immediately below it, an equivalent circuit could be obtained by eliminating all but the first two levels and connecting points A, B, C, and D to points A'', B'', C'', and D'' by the appropriate switch which formerly connected these points to

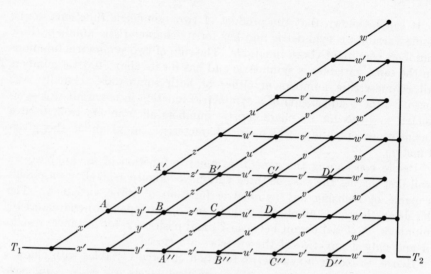

FIG. 4–39. Symmetric function; characteristic numbers 1, 3, and 5.

FIG. 4–40. Simplification of Fig. 4–39 by shifting down.

A', B', C', and D'. Then, instead of thinking of a path which rises an odd number of levels, we may describe the circuit as consisting of any path formed by an odd number of changes of level. We have as a result of this process of "shifting down," the diagram of Fig. 4–40, where the lower level corresponds to levels 0, 2, 4, and 6, and the upper level to the original levels 1, 3, and 5 simultaneously. The circuit is clearly equivalent to that of Fig. 4–39 but contains twenty switches instead of thirty-six.

This method can sometimes, with modifications, be applied to cases in which the characteristic numbers are not in arithmetic progression. In any case, it illustrates a possibility that should be kept in mind. The problem of the n-way light-switch control circuit can readily be solved by using this method.

EXERCISES

Draw as simple a circuit as possible for the symmetric functions given in Exercises 1 through 7.

1. $xy + yz + xz$. [Compare the symmetric circuit with a series-parallel circuit. Either can be done with five switches.]

2. $xyz'w' + xy'zw' + x'yzw' + xy'z'w + x'yz'w + x'y'zw.$

3. $abc' + ab'c + a'bc + ab'c' + a'bc' + a'b'c.$

4. A symmetric function of four variables with characteristic numbers 0 and 3.

5. A symmetric function of five variables with characteristic numbers 1 and 2.

6. A symmetric function of six variables with characteristic numbers 2, 4, and 6.

7. A symmetric function of six variables with characteristic numbers 0, 3, and 6.

8. In running a certain maze, a rat has the possibility of entering any one or more of four blind alleys. In each blind alley, there is an automatic device which closes a switch when the rat enters. Design a 6-terminal circuit to control five lights to count the errors that the rat makes. Use a typical symmetric-function diagram.

9. A light is to be controlled independently by any one of eight switches, one on each wall of an octagonal room. Using the shifting down method, design as simply as possible a circuit to control this light.

REFERENCES

CULBERTSON, *Mathematics and Logic for Digital Devices*, Van Nostrand, 1958.

KEISTER, RITCHIE, and WASHBURN, *The Design of Switching Circuits*, Van Nostrand, 1951.

NODELMAN and SMITH, *Mathematics for Electronics*, McGraw-Hill, 1956.

PHISTER, MONTGOMERY, *Logical Design of Digital Computers*, Wiley, 1958.

SHANNON, CLAUDE E., A Symbolic Analysis of Relay and Switching Circuits, *Trans. Am. Inst. Elec. Engrs.* **57** (1939).

CHAPTER 5

RELAY CIRCUITS AND CONTROL PROBLEMS

5–1 Introduction. In Chapter 4, we discussed switching circuits, and the type of switch used was thought of as a manually operated device that could be either open or closed. Although the material presented was equally applicable to circuits involving other bistable devices, many problems inherent in the type of device used were completely ignored. For instance, it was assumed possible to open one switch and close another simultaneously. Such idealizations are permissible in introducing a theory, but in an actual problem of design, considerably more care must be given to details of circuit operation. This is impossible without some discussion of the specific apparatus which is to be used. In this chapter, we will still be guilty of some disregard of details, but specific devices will be introduced to help minimize this shortcoming. In addition, the introduction of *relays* will allow us to design circuits with properties more complex and much more useful than would be possible if our circuits were limited to manually operated switches.

In certain parts of a circuit diagram, the type of switch used may be immaterial. We may even wish to use a manually operated switch. If such is the case, the notation of Chapter 4 may be used. In other cases, when the switch is to be operated by an electromagnet, a new notation will be introduced. Figure 5–1 illustrates this notation.

The term *contact* carries essentially the same meaning as *switch*, in that it is a device between two leads, which may be open or closed. However, we will think of a contact as a device consisting of (a) a spring, represented in the diagram as —o— when it is in rest position, to which one lead is connected, and (b) a point, represented in the diagram as ↑, to which the second lead is connected. By a *make* contact, we mean a contact that is *open* when the spring is at rest, and by a *break* contact, we mean one that is *closed* when the spring is at rest. A *transfer* contact is simply a combination of a make and a break contact operating from a single spring. In counting the number of contacts in a given circuit, a transfer contact will be counted as two contacts. Should it be possible to replace a separate make and break by a single transfer contact, we will consider this a simplification, since the second would usually be more economical to construct. For convenience, we will always use unprimed lower case italic letters, $x, y, a, \ldots$, to represent make contacts and primed letters, $x', y', a', \ldots$, to represent break contacts.

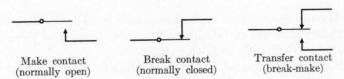

Make contact   Break contact   Transfer contact
(normally open)   (normally closed)   (break-make)

FIG. 5–1.   Circuit diagram conventions.

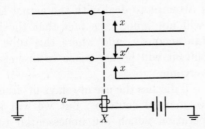

FIG. 5–2.   Relay with control circuit. This relay operates a transfer contact and a make contact simultaneously.

A *relay* is a combination of a certain set of contacts all operated by a single electromagnet. When no current passes through the coil of the magnet, all contact springs are at rest: make contacts are open, and break contacts are closed. When there is current through the winding of the coil, the relay is activated, and the conditions are reversed. The relay itself will be denoted by a capital italic letter, say X, all make contacts on X by x, and all break contacts on X by x'. We will be interested in circuits that involve the control of the relay as well as circuits that are formed through the contacts on the relay. In some cases, we will consider circuits in which the relay contacts are part of the control circuit for the relay itself. No such considerations were possible in Chapter 4, and this is one of the reasons for introducing relays. The "memory" feature of computing devices, for instance, depends on such circuits. Figure 5–2 indicates a typical relay, showing the control path of the electromagnet. The bar, designated by ¦, appearing between the contacts on X represents an insulated mechanical linkage, forcing the contacts to operate simultaneously. It does not carry current. The symbols ⊰ for ground and ⊣|⊢ for battery are the conventional ones. The control circuit consists of a single (manually operated) switch a.

There are many questions regarding the construction and operating characteristics of relays which will be purposefully avoided in this chapter. For instance, to decide what current source should be used in connection with a given relay, it would be necessary to inquire as to the amount of current necessary to operate the relay initially, the amount by which the current may be reduced after the relay has operated and still hold the relay in operation, and the current level at which the relay will definitely release. We will assume that current sources in our circuits have been correctly chosen and concentrate instead on those features of circuits which are related most directly to Boolean algebra.

Another problem related to relay operation involves the time interval between the closing of the circuit through the relay winding and the operation of the relay. A similar problem involves the release time of a relay. We will not attempt to deal with the actual lengths of these time intervals, but we will not ignore the fact that the intervals exist. No relay operates instantaneously, and where this time lag may affect the operation of a circuit, it will be necessary to discuss ways in which the difficulty can be overcome.

In summary, we will discuss the use of relays in circuits because they are more versatile than manual switches, but we will ignore many of the details of relay operation which are nonessential to the initial circuit design. Only those characteristics of relays which directly affect the Boolean functions representing the circuits involved will be considered.

5–2 Basic relay control paths. Before we can attempt to design circuits using relays to meet given sets of requirements, it is necessary to consider the ways in which a relay can be operated or released by an open or closed circuit which we will term a *control path*. In general, a relay circuit will be an interconnection of relays involving three types of circuits or paths. The first type of circuit will be termed an *input path*, which is a circuit consisting of switches or relays operated manually or by outside current sources, sources perhaps in a separate part of the machine being constructed. This is the part of the circuit by which instructions are given to the system as a whole. The second type of circuit, termed an *output path*, will usually be a circuit involving contacts on relays internal to the system. This is the part of the circuit which performs the task for which the circuit is constructed. The third type of circuit, associated with a given relay internal to the system, is called a *control path* and operates or releases the given relay only. It is helpful to think of a relay circuit in terms of these types of paths even though there is often considerable overlapping between them. For instance, a given input condition consisting of a current source or the state of a manually operated switch may well be a direct part of the output path. Control paths may be composed entirely from parts of input paths, may depend entirely on output paths of subcircuits designed to operate the relay, or may depend in part on the output paths of the circuit as a whole. These basic paths will be illustrated in the examples of this section and will be discussed in more detail in later sections.

Figure 5–3 illustrates a direct control path for a relay X, with two equivalent circuits. In this diagram, the relay is operated when switch a is closed, and released when a is opened. Here we would consider the input

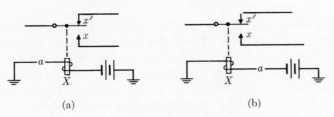

FIG. 5–3.   Direct control path of relay X.

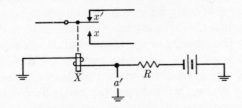

FIG. 5–4.   Shunt control path.

condition to be the state of switch a. No input path is shown, but an input path is involved if switch a is a contact on a relay Y, say, in which case the control path for the relay Y would be the input path for the circuit shown. Output paths may be formed by using either of the contacts operated by relay X. We would designate these contacts as x for the make and x' for the break contact.

Figure 5–4 shows a control path for relay X equivalent to that of Fig. 5–3, but in which the relay operates when the switch a' is opened. It may be convenient to employ such a path, called a *shunt path*, if the input condition is such as to require operation of a relay upon the opening of a circuit. There are disadvantages in the shunt path since the current through the closed path is wasted, and the resistor R introduced to minimize this loss is an added expense. Also, the release time of the relay is lengthened by a shunt control path. Note that whenever the function representing the shunt path is the negative of that used in a direct control path, the operation conditions for the relay are identical.

Figure 5–5 shows a control path for a relay X in which the relay itself affects its own control path. Such a control path is called a *locking circuit*, and if switch b is closed (once a has been closed to cause initial operation

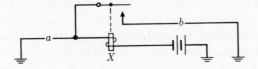

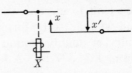

FIG. 5–5.   Locking path.   FIG. 5–6.   Continuity transfer (make-break).

of X), the relay will remain operated until such a time as b is opened, regardless of the state of a. This is the basic "memory" device in a relay circuit, which allows a relay to maintain its operated state after the input condition causing operation has disappeared. In this figure, no output paths are shown but could be formed from other contacts operated by relay X. We can consider the control path for this relay as consisting partly of an input path (switch a), and partly of an output path (the contact on X), which illustrates the fact pointed out earlier that there is no clear-cut division of a circuit into input, output, and control paths.

In a transfer contact, it is sometimes important that the make contact be closed prior to the opening of the break contact. Such a transfer can be constructed, and is called a *continuity transfer* (or a *make-break contact*). It is sufficient for our purposes to know that such a transfer can be built; for the interested reader, we indicate the method of construction in the diagram convention given in Fig. 5–6. Other special devices, involving several break and make contacts, are available to operate the contacts in a variety of orders.

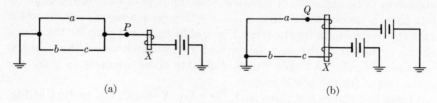

(a)   (b)

FIG. 5–7. Relay operated by $a + bc$.

Several variations in these basic control paths are possible, and some will be introduced later when needed. Other arrangements of contacts may be more suitable than these for special purposes, but these illustrate the basic notions of relay control and operation.

One more control path will be shown to illustrate some additional possibilities in a control circuit. First, suppose that a control path is to be designed in such a way that a relay X operates if switch a is closed or if both switches b and c are closed. A suitable control circuit is shown in Fig. 5–7(a). Suppose that it is desired to use switch a in another part of the circuit as well. If point P were to be connected to another circuit, the desired lead to ground would be formed if a were closed, but a lead to ground would also be formed if b and c were both closed. To avoid this difficulty, a doubly wound relay might be used to isolate a from bc, as shown in Fig. 5–7(b). A lead from point Q may be used to include a in another part of the circuit.

When a manually operated switch is used in a circuit, it will be convenient to distinguish between two types of switches. The first, which we will continue to refer to simply as a *switch*, will be so designed that it can be left in either open or closed position. The second, which we will refer to as a *key*, will be thought of as a switch subject to a spring that may be manually depressed to change the state of one or more contacts on the key, but which will automatically return to its initial position when released. That is, a key will work exactly like a relay except that it is operated manually rather than by an electromagnet.

EXAMPLE 1. A circuit A has been constructed to realize a certain function f. It is now desired to realize f'. Show how A may be used to obtain the desired circuit. Ignore the operate and release time for the relay used.

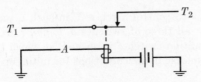

FIGURE 5–8

Solution. Since f' is a function which is 0 when f is 1 and conversely, the function f_{12} in Fig. 5–8 is clearly equal to f', since the path from T_1 to T_2 is closed when A is open (relay released) and open when A is closed (relay operated).

EXAMPLE 2. A relay X is to be operated when either of two switches y and z is closed, but not when both y and z are closed. Once operated, the relay is to remain in operation until a key K is depressed, at which time it is to release, regardless of the states of switches y and z.

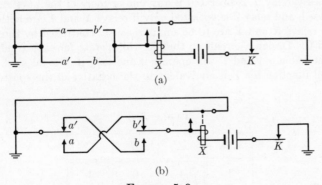

(a)

(b)

FIGURE 5–9

Solution. Referring to Fig. 5–5, a in the diagram must be replaced by a circuit which realizes the function $f = xy' + x'y$ to satisfy the requirements for initial operation. Now a locking path is needed, as in Fig. 5–5, but if key K were inserted in place of b, the relay would not release at any time when f had the value 1. K will cause the release of the relay under any circumstances if it is introduced as indicated in Fig. 5–9(a). Figure 5–9(b) is equivalent to Fig. 5–9(a), but uses a different notation for the switches a and b.

EXERCISES

1. (a) Draw the circuit realizing the function $f = a + bc$.

(b) Draw a control circuit for a relay X so that X will operate if and only if the circuit in part (a) is closed.

(c) Draw the output circuit from relay X which realizes f'. [Include this in the circuit diagram of part (b).]

2. Draw the circuit which realizes the function $f = a(b + c) + d$. Use this circuit to control two relays X and Y simultaneously, so that X is operated if and only if the circuit is closed, and Y is operated if and only if the circuit is open.

3. Draw the circuit to control a relay X in such a way that it will operate initially if any one or all three of switches a, b, and c are closed, and will then remain in operation until a switch d is opened, at which time it will release, except that it will not release if the conditions for initial operation are satisfied at the time.

4. A relay X is to be operated when a key A (equipped with a break contact) is depressed and remain operated until a key B (equipped with a break contact) is depressed, at which time it will release, regardless of the state of key A. Design the control circuit.

5. Three switches a, b, and c are to control a relay X so that the relay is operated if any one or all three of a, b, and c are closed and is released when no one or only two of a, b, and c are closed. Design the control circuit.

6. Three relays X, Y, and Z are to be controlled by keys A, B, and C, each equipped with makes, breaks, or transfer contacts as needed. Design a control circuit such that relay X is operated only while A and B are depressed and C is not depressed, relay Y is operated if any one or more of the keys A, B, and C are depressed, and relay Z is operated only if relays X and Y are both operated.

7. Two relays X and Y are to be simultaneously controlled by three switches A, B, and C. Design a circuit so that X will operate for each combination of switches in Table 5–1 and Y will operate if and only if X is released. (That is, the control function for Y is equivalent to the negative of the control function for X.)

TABLE 5–1

Row	A	B	C
1	1	0	1
2	1	0	0
3	1	1	0
4	0	0	1

5–3 n-terminal circuits and the uses of transfer contacts. When two or more relays are to be controlled from common inputs, n-terminal circuits arise naturally from the attempt to be economical in the use of contacts.

Such circuits are of the type discussed in Section 4–6. In this section, we will use a number of examples to illustrate methods which may be used in designing control circuits and to show difficulties which may arise.

EXAMPLE 1. Two relays X and Y are to be controlled from contacts on relays A, B, C, and D representing input conditions. We are to design a control circuit such that X will be operated when A is operated and B is released, and Y will be operated if both A and C are operated or if D is released.

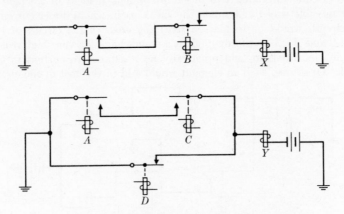

FIG. 5–10. Separate control circuits for two relays.

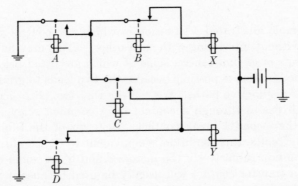

FIG. 5–11. Combined control circuits involving a sneak path.

Solution. Denote the control function for X by $x(a, b)$, and for Y by $y(a, c, d)$. From the given conditions, $x(a, b) = ab'$ and $y(a, c, d) = ac + d'$. The separate circuits are shown in Fig. 5–10. These circuits would require two make contacts on relay A if drawn separately, but may be combined as in Fig. 5–11 with only a single make. This small saving in contacts would become significant if, instead of a single contact a, the common part of the circuits were a more complicated circuit. The difficulty in this circuit is that relay X will now operate if C is operated while B and D are released, which was not intended. Such a path is termed a *sneak path*. We can eliminate this sneak path with the use of a transfer contact on D, as illustrated in Fig. 5–12. Since the path through A and C is important only when D is operated, the circuit is equivalent. Or, we may show this algebraically since $y(a, c, d) = ac + d' = acd + d'$, where the second expression represents the new path. Even though this last circuit uses an extra contact on D, a reduction in total number of contacts would result if A represented a circuit containing two or more contacts instead of a single contact. Another possible way to eliminate the sneak path, where direct current is used in the circuit, would be to place a *rectifying diode* in the circuit of Fig. 5–11 between C and A. A rectifying diode is a device having a very high resistance to current in one direction, and practically no resistance to current in the other direction. Of course, such an element would add to the cost of the circuit.

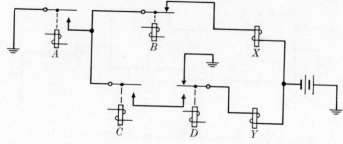

Fig. 5–12. Combined circuit with sneak path eliminated by a transfer contact.

This example illustrated a situation in which two control paths can be combined without interfering with each other. (This may happen in any of several sets of circumstances, some of which are listed below.) In this case, the combination is possible because the two leads to ground for relay Y consist of disjunctive paths. We will say that two paths are *disjunctive* if each path passes through a contact on a common relay, one using a make and the second a break contact. In terms of the functions representing the circuits, this condition is equivalent to the condition that two functions contain respectively the factors a and a' for some relay A. In such cases a transfer contact will usually be used because it requires one less spring and ensures that the two paths cannot be simultaneously closed. With separate make and break contacts, it is possible that the circuits would be simultaneously closed for a short time due to contact stagger, allowing the make to close before the break opens.

Three simple cases in which two control paths may be combined without sneak paths are listed below. Let the corresponding control functions be f and g, the functions representing the control paths for relays X and Y respectively.

I. f and g contain common factors.

EXAMPLE 2. Suppose that $f = (ab + a'b')c$ and that $g = (ab + a'b')d$. The combined circuit is given in Fig. 5–13.

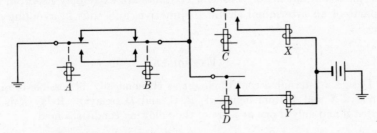

FIG. 5–13.   Combined control paths $(ab + a'b')c$ and $(ab + a'b')d$.

II. Summands of f and g contain common factors, and these summands are disjunctive.

EXAMPLE 3. Suppose that $f = (a + b)c + d$ and that $g = (a + b)c' + e$. Since $(a + b)c$ and $(a + b)c'$ are disjunctive, the circuits may be combined as in Fig. 5–14.

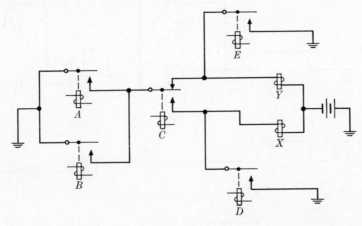

FIG. 5–14.   Combined control paths $(a + b)c + d$ and $(a + b)c' + e$.

III. Summands of f and g contain common factors, and this summand of f (or of g) is disjunctive with the remaining summand of f (or of g).

EXAMPLE 4. We need only refer to Example 1, where $x(a, b)$ and $y(a, c, d)$ illustrate such control functions, and the circuits of Fig. 5–12 show the method of construction, using a transfer contact.

In summary, we can say that two or more 2-terminal control circuits may often be combined in part with a net saving of contacts. Possible combinations can be spotted by examining the Boolean functions representing the circuits. In combining control circuits, sneak paths should be avoided unless it is known that the combination leading to closure of the sneak path will not arise. Transfer contacts are extremely useful in keeping parts of an n-terminal circuit disjunctive, and thus in avoiding sneak paths.

EXERCISES

1. Design a 3-terminal control circuit as economically as possible to operate two relays X and Y from inputs A, B, C, and D (relays). Relay X is to be operated if and only if one or more of the following conditions hold:

   (a) A operated and B released,   (b) C operated,   (c) D operated.

Relay Y is to be operated if and only if one or more of the following conditions hold:

   (d) A operated, B and D released,   (e) C operated and D released.

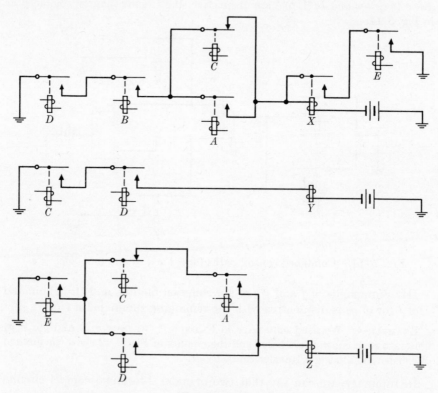

FIGURE 5–15

2. Design a 4-terminal circuit to control relays X, Y, and Z from input relays A, B, C, and D under the following conditions (nine contacts are sufficient). X is to be operated if and only if one or more of the following conditions hold:

(a) A and C operated, B released,   (b) B and C operated, A released,

(c) D operated.

Y is to be operated if and only if one or more of the following conditions hold:

(d) A operated, B, C, and D released,

(e) B operated, A, C, and D released.

Z is to be operated if and only if the following condition holds:

(f) A operated, B and C released.

3. Use the idea of a transfer tree to design a 4-terminal network to control the three relays X, Y, and Z if the control functions of these relays are given as follows. (The functions refer to input relays A, B, C, and D.)

(a) X is controlled by the function $f = abcd' + ab'cd' + a'bc'd'$,

(b) Y is controlled by the function $g = a'bcd' + ab'c'd' + a'b'c'd'$,

(c) Z is controlled by the function $h = abc'd' + a'b'cd'$.

4. Combine and simplify the circuits controlling relays X, Y, and Z as shown in Fig. 5–15.

5. Design a multiterminal network for controlling three relays X, Y, and Z from input relays A, B, C, and D subject to the conditions given in Table 5–2. The symbol 1 corresponds to the operated state of the relay, the symbol 0 to the released state.

TABLE 5–2

Row	A	B	C	D	X	Y	Z
1	1	1	1	1	1	0	1
2	1	1	1	0	1	1	0
3	1	1	0	1	1	0	0
4	1	1	0	0	1	0	0
5	1	0	1	1	0	1	1
6	1	0	1	0	0	1	0
7	1	0	0	1	0	1	0
8	1	0	0	0	0	1	0
9	0	1	1	1	0	0	1
10	0	1	1	0	0	1	0
11	0	1	0	1	0	0	0
12	0	1	0	0	0	0	0
13	0	0	1	1	0	0	1
14	0	0	1	0	0	1	0
15	0	0	0	1	0	0	0
16	0	0	0	0	0	0	0

5–4 Operate and hold paths. Figure 5–16 illustrates the most general kind of control circuit for the operation of a singly wound relay X. It consists of two circuits, the first of which we will refer to as the *operate path*. This is the circuit which represents the conditions for which it is desired that the relay will operate initially. In the figure, this circuit is shown as a single letter A, which may correspond to a single contact or to a complicated circuit. The second circuit controlling the operation of the relay X, which we will refer to as the *hold path*, represents those conditions for which it is desired that the relay will remain in operation after once being operated. This circuit will always contain a make contact on relay X and may contain a circuit in series with this contact, designated by the single letter B in the figure.

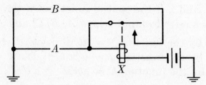

FIG. 5–16.   General operate and hold paths for a relay X.

Normally, the conditions for which the relay is to operate and those for which it is to hold are given separately, and the circuit design is begun by considering the corresponding functions separately.   After initial simplifications of operate and hold paths have been performed, it may be possible to effect combinations of these paths in such a way as to lead to further simplifications, as we will see presently.   From Fig. 5–16, it is apparent that the function F representing the conditions controlling relay X may be written as $F = f_o + xf_h$, where f_o is the function representing the operate path A and f_h is the function representing the hold path B.

EXAMPLE 1.   A relay X is to be controlled in the following way from inputs $A, B, C, D,$ and E.

X is to operate initially if and only if one or more of the following conditions are satisfied:

(a) $B, D,$ and E are operated; A and C are released,
(b) $B, C, D,$ and E are operated; A is released,
(c) $B, C,$ and E are operated; A and D are released,
(d) B and E are operated; $A, C,$ and D are released,
(e) C and E are operated; $A, B,$ and D are released,
(f) $A, C,$ and E are operated; D and B are released,
(g) $A, B, C,$ and E are operated; D is released.

In addition, X is to remain operated if one or more of the following conditions are satisfied. [Note that the relay will hold for all operate conditions as well. Hence duplication of (a) through (g) is unnecessary.]

TABLE 5–3

(a) OPERATE

Row	A	B	C	D	E
1	0	1	0	1	1
2	0	1	1	1	1
3	0	1	1	0	1
4	0	1	0	0	1
5	0	0	1	0	1
6	1	0	1	0	1
7	1	1	1	0	1

(b) HOLD

Row	A	B	C	D	E
1	1	0	1	0	0
2	1	1	1	0	0
3	1	0	1	0	1
4	1	1	1	0	1

(h) A and C are operated; B, D, and E are released,

(i) A, B, and C are operated; D and E are released.

It is awkward to visualize all these conditions at once, but if we use a table to represent the conditions, they are much easier to work with. Tables 5–3(a) and (b) are of the same type as those in Sections 4–5 and 4–6 except that the only rows shown are those corresponding to the combinations for which the function assumes the value 1. All other combinations correspond to the value 0 for the function. Since the inputs will be interpreted as controlling relays, the symbols 0 and 1 refer to the states of relays, a slight extension of the earlier interpretations. 1 will signify that the relay is in the operated state, 0 that it is in the released state.

The first two rows of Table 5–3(b) represent the given hold conditions. The last two rows are duplications of rows 6 and 7 of Table (a), representing operate conditions, which are included in Table (b) to aid in simplifying the corresponding function. Note that it does no harm for the hold circuit to be closed for any or all combinations involved in the operate circuit (whether specifically given as hold conditions or not), since the relay will be operated for these conditions anyway.

To determine f_o, we note that rows 1, 2, 3, and 4 of Table 5–3(a) are alike except for columns C and D. Similarly, rows 3, 5, 6, and 7 are alike except for columns A and B. The correct function is $f_o = a'be + cd'e = (a'b + cd')e$. Here row 3 was used twice to make the resulting function as simple as possible. The law of tautology for Boolean algebra justifies this. It is necessary to use each row at least once, but any row may be used as often as desired.

To determine f_h, we note that in Table 5–3(b), rows 1, 2, 3, and 4 are alike except for columns B and E. The correct function is therefore $f_h = acd'$. The control function for relay X may then be written as $F = (a'b + cd')e + xacd'$. If we add the zero term $xaa'b$, we may factor F as follows:

$$F = (a'b + cd')(e + xa).$$

The circuit diagram is given in Fig. 5–17, making use of the factor that is common to the operate and hold paths, as shown above. The methods and examples of Section 5–3 apply here as well as to circuits that control separate relays.

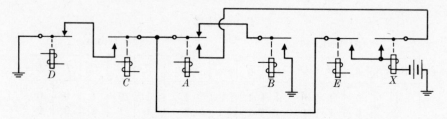

FIG. 5–17.   Control circuit of Example 1.

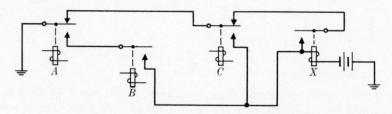

FIG. 5–18.   Control circuit of Example 2.

EXAMPLE 2. If we suppose that the function representing the control circuit for a relay is $F = ab + a'c + x(a'c')$, then the circuit may be drawn as in Fig. 5–18, where the break contact on A is common to the hold and operate paths, and a transfer contact on C is used to ensure that the paths are disjunctive.

EXERCISES

1. Design and draw a control circuit for a relay X as simply as possible so that the relay will operate and hold for the conditions given in Table 5–4. A, B, and C are input relays. Show the Boolean function representing the control circuit. (This circuit can be drawn with six contacts.)

2. Draw the simplest possible control circuit for a relay X to be operated and held under the conditions given in Table 5–5 on four relays A, B, C, and D, each controlled by input paths. Show the Boolean function representing the control circuits.

3. The control circuit for a relay X is represented by the function $F = ab' + bc + abx$, where a, b, and c refer to contacts on input relays A, B, and C, respectively. Draw the simplest possible circuit diagram.

4. The control circuit for a relay Y is represented by the function $F = ab + ab' + a'b + a'by$. Draw the control circuit.

5. Draw the simplest possible control circuit for a relay X to be operated and held under the conditions given in Table 5–6 on four input relays A, B, C, and D. Show the Boolean function representing the circuit.

TABLE 5–4

(a) OPERATE

Row	A	B	C
1	1	0	1
2	0	1	0
3	0	0	1

(b) HOLD

Row	A	B	C
1	1	1	1
2	1	1	0
3	1	0	0
4	0	1	1
5	0	0	0

TABLE 5–5

(a) OPERATE

Row	A	B	C	D
1	1	1	1	0
2	1	1	0	0
3	1	1	0	1
4	1	0	1	1
5	1	0	1	0
6	1	1	1	1

(b) HOLD

Row	A	B	C	D
1	1	0	0	1
2	1	0	0	0

TABLE 5–6

(a) OPERATE

Row	A	B	C	D
1	1	1	0	0
2	1	0	1	1
3	1	1	0	1
4	1	0	1	0

(b) HOLD

Row	A	B	C	D
1	1	0	0	1
2	1	1	1	0

5–5 Sequential circuits and sequence diagrams. Until now we have concentrated primarily upon circuits in which all relays or switches were assumed to operate simultaneously. We have disregarded the time interval between the closing of a relay control path and the closing of the relay contacts, called the *operate time* of the relay; similarly, we have ignored the *release time* of a relay, that is, the delay between the opening of the control circuit and the opening of the relay contacts. This idealization has simplified the problem of design of relay circuits, and in many applications these delays are of no serious consequence. Often, however, these time delays cannot be ignored, and sometimes the delays that cause relays to operate in sequence, rather than simultaneously, can be used to ad-

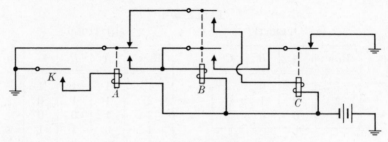

FIG. 5–19. A sequential circuit.

vantage to perform tasks that would be impossible otherwise. In many applications, a timing device for introducing sequential signals is an essential part of the design. In this section, we will consider some circuits that operate sequentially and charts for representing their operation. In the next section, we will discuss the design of such circuits.

A circuit in which time is important, and in which two or more things happen in sequence will be termed a *sequential circuit*. Such a circuit is shown in Fig. 5–19. In this diagram, if key K is depressed and held down momentarily, relay A is operated first. In operating, A closes the lead to ground on the winding of B, which causes B to operate, which locks B through a break contact on C. If now K is released, relay A releases, closing the control path of C. C, in operating, breaks the hold path on B, causing B to release, and this in turn releases C. The relays now will remain in released position until K is again depressed.

The operation of this sequential circuit can be summarized in a *sequence diagram* as in Fig. 5–20. The width of each column corresponds to the length of the operate or release time of the relay involved. It is often the case that the exact size of these time intervals is less important than the sequence of events to which they correspond. In Fig. 5–20, the interval in which each relay is operated is occupied by a horizontal line opposite the appropriate symbol for the relay. An empty interval is usually given on both ends of such a diagram if a state ever occurs in which all relays are released.

	Time interval								
	1	2	3	4	5	6	7	8	9
Key: K		▬	▬	▬					
Relays: A			▬	▬	▬				
B					▬	▬	▬		
C							▬	▬	

FIG. 5–20. Sequence chart for the circuit of Fig. 5–19.

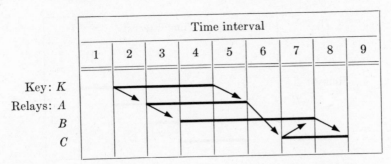

Key: K
Relays: A
B
C

FIG. 5–21. Sequence chart for the circuit of Fig. 5–19, showing control.

To help to represent the action of the circuit, arrows are often drawn to indicate the immediate cause of each change of state of each relay. For example, in the circuit shown in Fig. 5–19, operation of K causes the operation of A, and release of A causes C to operate. The appropriate arrows for the sequence diagram of this circuit are shown in Fig. 5–21.

Figure 5–19 indeed illustrates a sequential circuit, but the circuit does not perform any function; that is, there is no indicated output. On the other hand, the circuit of Fig. 5–22 does have an output, in the form of a light which shines during the time that relay C is operated and A is released. This output could equally well be a signal to another part of the circuit, to be used for any of a number of purposes other than providing a light. Another feature of this circuit is that it automatically recycles itself; that is, it will go through the same sequence of states repeatedly until a part fails or the current supply is cut off.

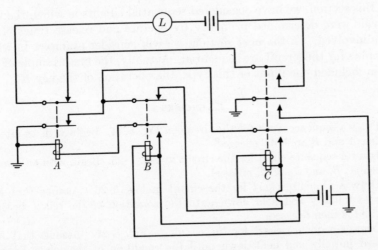

FIG. 5–22. An automatically recycling sequential circuit with output.

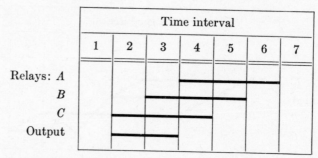

Fig. 5–23. Sequence diagram for the circuit of Fig. 5–22.

To construct the sequence diagram for this circuit, let us assume an initial state in which all relays are released. C is operated first, through breaks on A and B, and will be held until A operates. In operating, C closes the operate path of B. B, in operating, closes the operate path of A, causing A to operate, which in turn breaks the hold path on C. In releasing, C causes the release of B, which then causes A to release. Now with all relays released, C will again be operated, and the cycle is repeated as before. The output is wired through a make on C and a break on A, causing the light to shine during the required intervals. The sequence chart is given in Fig. 5–23.

It may happen in operating, or in releasing, that a particular relay simultaneously controls two other relays. Such a condition is termed a *race condition* and should be avoided in constructing sequential circuits if the sequence in which the two relays operate affects the remainder of the circuit. Where this cannot be avoided, two relays with significantly different operate (or release) times may be used.

In this section, we have considered sequential circuits in which the time intervals were determined primarily by operate and release times of the relays involved. In the next section, we will consider examples in which the inputs for the circuit are sequential. Actually, the first example of this section included one input of this type, the operation of the key K.

Exercises

1. Draw a sequence chart for the circuit in Fig. 5–24. Begin with an interval in which A and B are both released.

2. Draw a sequence chart for the circuit in Fig. 5–25. Begin with an interval in which A, B, and C are all released.

3. Draw a sequence chart for the circuit in Fig. 5–26. Assume that K is depressed initially and held down until the condition of the relays becomes stable and is then released.

4. Draw a sequence chart for the circuit in Fig. 5–27. Assume that K is depressed initially and held down until the condition of the relays becomes stable and is then released.

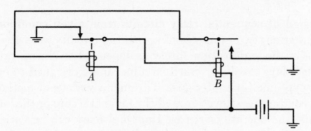

FIGURE 5–24

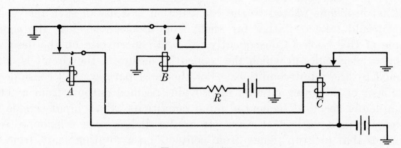

FIGURE 5–25

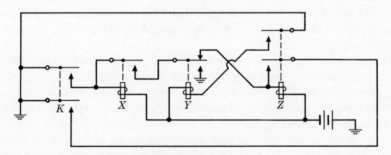

FIGURE 5–26

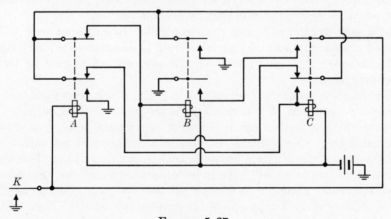

FIGURE 5–27

5–6 Design of sequential relay circuits from given conditions. In the preceding section, two examples of sequential circuits were given in which the lengths of the various time intervals depended on the operate or release time of the relays involved. Such circuits can be designed to operate with reasonably specific time intervals. Through a variety of methods, such as the use of conducting sleeves around the magnetic core or the incorporation of dashpots, the operate or release time of a relay can be varied from less than five milliseconds up to an interval of several seconds. Thermal relays provide time delays up to thirty seconds. We could cite many special problems related to the construction and use of such relays, but this would take us rather far afield from Boolean algebra, the central topic of this book. Consequently, we will concentrate on the design of sequential circuits in which the sequential nature of the circuit is determined by the input conditions. For the most part, we will consider the problem of designing circuits to provide specified outputs from a set of completely specified sequential input conditions. Such input signals can originate in a variety of ways—from the dialing of a telephone, from brushes that pick up signals from contacts on a rotating shaft, from the output of a sequential circuit in another part of the device being designed, etc. We will not be concerned here with the source of input information, but with the design of a required sequential output from given input conditions.

In a *combinational circuit*, each occurrence of a specified set of input conditions produces the same output. In a *sequential circuit*, this is not always the case. We will construct circuits for which the *sequence* of inputs (rather than the *combination* of input conditions that might hold at a given time) is the determining factor. It will be necessary to construct circuits capable of remembering past sets of conditions as well as of interpreting existing conditions. To provide the needed memory feature will require, in addition to relays controlled by input conditions, the introduction of new relays to be controlled in part by hold paths.

In a sequential circuit, any relay controlled by an input path will be termed a *primary relay*. Relays introduced in addition to primary relays, and controlled through contacts on the primary relays, will be termed *secondary relays*.

Consider the sequence diagram of Fig. 5–28, which represents both the sequential operation of two primary relays and a desired output. The output, which is to be a signal provided by a closed path, is to occur in interval 3 only. Note that a combinational circuit will not suffice since the same input combination occurs in both intervals 3 and 5. This means that a secondary relay will have to be introduced to differentiate between these intervals. Figure 5–29 shows a suitable choice of intervals in which the secondary relay X may operate to provide this service. Note that the

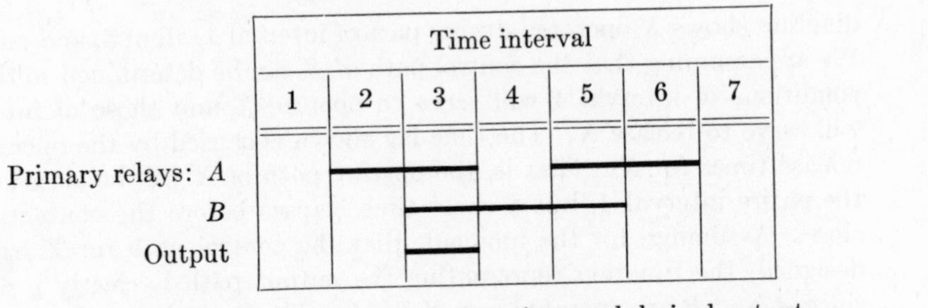

Time interval
1
2
3
4
5
6
7
Primary relays: A
B
Output

FIG. 5-28. Sequence of primary relay operations and desired output.

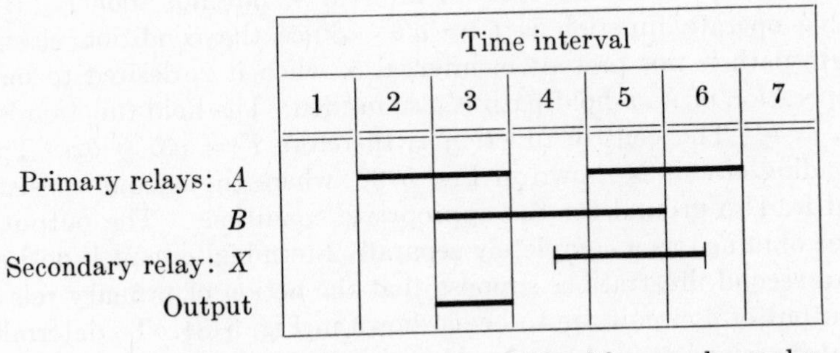

Time interval
1
2
3
4
5
6
7
Primary relays: A
B
Secondary relay: X
Output

FIG. 5-29. Sequence diagram of Fig. 5-28 with secondary relay.

Output
B
A
X

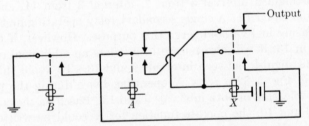

FIG. 5-30. Circuit for the diagram of Fig. 5-29.

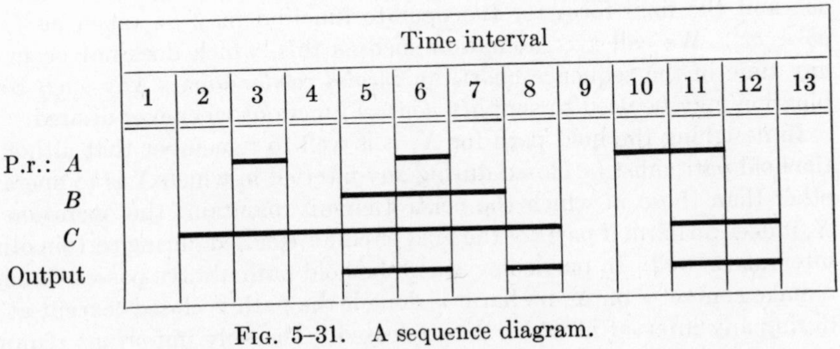

Time interval
1
2
3
4
5
6
7
8
9
10
11
12
13
P.r.: A
B
C
Output

FIG. 5-31. A sequence diagram.

diagram shows X operated during part of interval 4, all of 5, and part of 6. We are assuming that the control path of X can be determined so that the conditions of interval 4 will serve to operate X and those of interval 6 will serve to release X. The time lag shown is caused by the operate and release times for X. That is, the operate path of X will be closed during the entire interval 4, but a short time elapses before the contacts on X close. Assuming, for the moment, that the control path for X has been designed, the function representing the output path is clearly $g = abx'$, since A and B are operated and X is released only in interval 3.

The control path for X can be designed in two parts, as discussed earlier. The operate path should close in interval 4, but not sooner. Hence a suitable operate function is $f_o = a'b$. Since the condition closing the operate path is not present in interval 5, when it is desired to maintain the operation of X, a hold path is also needed. The hold function is given by $f_h = b$. The control function is therefore $F = a'b + bx$. The corresponding circuit is shown in Fig. 5–30, where the output consists of a closed lead to ground for the appropriate conditions. The output could also be obtained as a completely separate 2-terminal circuit if desired.

As a second illustration, suppose that the action of primary relays and the output of a circuit are to be as shown in Fig. 5–31. To determine the secondary relays needed for the desired output, note that it will be necessary to distinguish interval 5 from 7, interval 3 from 11, and intervals 2 and 4 from 8 and 12. A single secondary relay operating first in interval 6 and releasing in 13 would serve this purpose. However, if the relay is to release in 13, it will also release in 9 unless an additional relay is provided to distinguish between intervals 9 and 13. To avoid this, we have indicated in Fig. 5–32 a relay X operating twice during the time of the chart, and releasing in both intervals 9 and 13. Based on the conditions of intervals 6 and 10, the operate function for X could be written as $f_o = abc + ab'c'$. However, the combination A and B operated, C released never occurs, so the term abc' will not affect the circuit; and $abc' + abc = ab$, which allows us to simplify f_o to $ab + ab'c'$. Similarly, $ab'c' + abc' = ac'$, and the final form for the operate function may be taken as $f_o = ab + ac'$. We call a combination such as this, which does not occur at any time in the sequence chart, an *invalid combination*. Any such combination may be used to simplify control functions whenever desired.

In designing the hold path for X, it is well to remember that although the hold path must be closed during any interval in which X is to operate, other than those in which the control circuit maintains the operation of X, it does no harm if parts of the hold circuit are closed during certain other intervals as well. In particular, since the hold path always passes through a make contact x on X, no harm is done if the path is closed (except at x) during any interval in which X is released. The only important require-

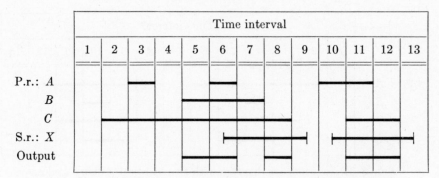

	Time interval												
	1	2	3	4	5	6	7	8	9	10	11	12	13
P.r.: A													
B													
C													
S.r.: X													
Output													

FIG. 5–32. The diagram of Fig. 5–31, with secondary relay added.

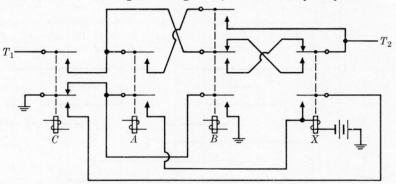

FIG. 5–33. Circuit for the diagram of Fig. 5–32.

ment on the hold path is that it must open during each interval in which X is to release.

According to the specifications given in Fig. 5–32, X is to release just after each release of C, and C is operated in each interval during which the hold path must be closed. Hence a simple hold function is $f_h = c$. Combining the operate and hold functions, we obtain the control function for X as $F = a(b + c') + cx$.

The output path is now just a combinational circuit closed under the conditions represented in intervals 5, 6, 8, 11, and 12. Five conditions are involved (even though intervals 8 and 12 are alike) because the operation of X changes during interval 6. The output function is therefore given by $g = bcx' + abc + b'cx$. The circuit showing both the control of X and the output path is given in Fig. 5–33. The output is the 2-terminal circuit joining T_1 to T_2.

As these examples show, the first steps in designing a circuit to meet the output requirements on a sequential diagram are to decide how many secondary relays will be needed and to determine a suitable operating sequence for these relays. Once this has been done, the control paths of

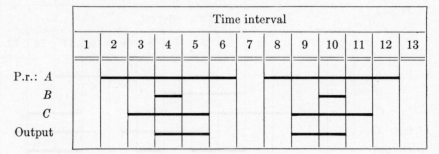

Fig. 5–34.   A sequence diagram with two identical primary cycles.

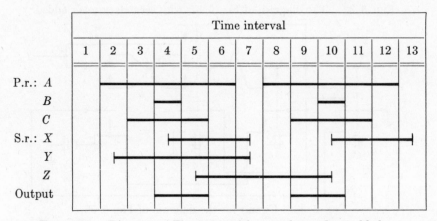

Fig. 5–35.   Diagram of Fig. 5–34, with secondary relays added.

secondary relays can be designed with the help of Boolean functions, or in simple cases, by inspection. The output path is then simply a combinational circuit.

As a third example, consider the sequence chart of Fig. 5–34, in which a particular sequence of inputs occurs twice and the output is different in the two cases. To write a suitable output function, it will be necessary to distinguish between the first and second sequences of operation and to distinguish between intervals 3 and 5 in the first sequence, and again between 9 and 11 in the second.

In attempting to determine the number of secondary relays needed, there is no formal approach which will give an immediate answer. We can say in general that n relays can distinguish between at most 2^n identical combinations of inputs. However, the problem of possible control for these secondary relays may complicate the situation and require one or more additional relays for control purposes only.

In Fig. 5–35, one choice of operating sequence is shown for three secondary relays, which are sufficient for this diagram. (For another possible

TABLE 5–7

OUTPUT CONDITIONS FOR THE DIAGRAM OF FIG. 5–35

Row	A	B	C	X	Y
1	1	1	1	—	—
2	1	0	1	1	1
3	1	0	1	0	0

sequence, see Exercise 3 at the end of this section.) First, relay X is added to distinguish between intervals 3 and 5 and between intervals 9 and 11. The control of this relay will be a simple matter since it is to operate when B is operated, and to release when A releases. The control function may be written as $F_x = b + ax$.

Next, relay Y is added to distinguish the first cycle of A, B, and C from the second. However, with this operating sequence for Y, the control of Y cannot be managed from A, B, C, and X alone, since the relay would operate again in interval 8. To distinguish interval 2 from 8, a third relay Z is introduced. The operate condition for Y is A operated, B, C, and Z released. Y must then hold until all three are released. A suitable control function is $F_y = ac'z'x' + ay$. The operate condition for Z is A, C, X, and Y operated, B released, and Z is to hold until B is operated. The control function may be written as $F_z = ab'cxy + b'z$. The race condition between the release of X and Y in interval 7 does not affect Z since Z will hold for as long as B is released.

Table 5–7 represents the output conditions. Note that the output is dependent on A, B, C, X, and Y only. Z is used only in controlling Y. The dashes in row 1 indicate that the states of X and Y are not needed to determine output in intervals 4 and 8, since these are the only two intervals in which A, B, and C are all operated. The output function is $g = b + c(xy + x'y')$. The circuit for this diagram is not shown, but can be readily drawn from these functions. There are other sequences for secondary relays which might work equally well, or better.

In summary, the procedure for the design of a sequential circuit from a given sequence chart is first to determine, by trial and error, the number of secondary relays needed. In connection with this, the secondary relays must be introduced in such a sequence as to make distinctions between like combinations of inputs which affect the desired outputs. Finally, the control circuits for secondary relays and the output circuits are designed. Much of this is of necessity done by inspection of the sequence chart. The choice of operating sequence for secondary relays is determined in part from conditions which lead to simple control circuits. Boolean algebra

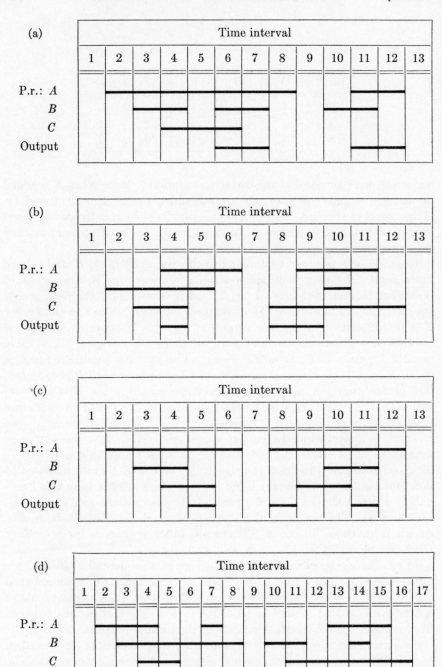

FIGURE 5–36

is convenient for writing the control and output functions, but unfortunately, the algebra alone is not sufficiently versatile to represent the entire problem. As we have seen, Boolean functions correspond only to those parts of the design which are combinational in nature. Sequential operation is handled primarily by the ingenuity of the designer. This section was included, not primarily as an application of the algebra, but as an extension of earlier sections to show the limitations of Boolean algebra in design problems and to illustrate the versatility of relay circuits.

EXERCISES

1. Draw the circuit for Fig. 5–35.

2. Introduce the necessary secondary relays to secure the required output for each of the sequence diagrams in Fig. 5–36. Construct a new sequence diagram in each case showing the operation of all secondary relays used. Write the Boolean functions for the control of each secondary relay and for the output. Draw the circuit diagrams, showing all secondary relays and the output for Fig. 5–36(a).

3. Only two secondary relays X and Y are necessary for the output of Fig. 5–34, provided that each depends upon the other for its control. Select such a sequence and write the control and output functions.

4. Given the sequence diagram of Fig. 5–37, introduce the necessary secondary relays and write the control and output functions.

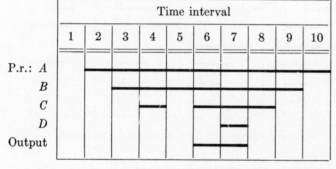

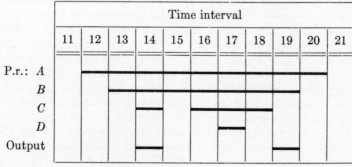

FIGURE 5–37

5–7 Special problems involving the design of relay circuits. This final section on relay circuits contains two examples in which the sequence diagram is not given but the situation calls for the construction of a sequence diagram as part of the solution to the problem. This situation is more realistic than those of Section 5–6 and corresponds closely to the problem which faces the designer in practical applications of the techniques we have presented.

Suppose that it is desired to obtain four or more signals from two keys in such a way that no signal is given when both keys are in released position. Combinational circuits alone will not solve the problem since there are only four states possible for two switches and one of these (both released) is specifically excluded. Sequential signals, using secondary relays, must therefore be used. The problem is made more specific in the following example.

EXAMPLE 1. Design a sequential circuit to cause four lights, red, white, blue, and green, respectively, to flash individually.

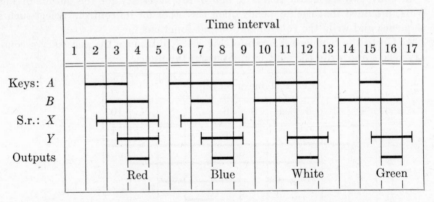

FIG. 5–38. Sequence diagram for four signals from two keys.

Solution. Many sequential inputs could be chosen, but those of Fig. 5–38 are a reasonable choice. The input combinations based on keys A and B are simple enough to be easily learned, but complex enough to make control of secondary relays easy. The four sequences are the signals in time intervals 2–4, 6–8, 10–12, and 14–16, respectively. An interval in which both keys are released is shown between each sequence since we will permit the sequences to occur in an arbitrary order. Because of this, it is necessary to cause all secondary relays, as well, to release in intervals 5, 9, 13, and 17. A suitable sequence of operation is shown for secondary relays X and Y which will distinguish between the four signals. The red light will be controlled by an output in 4, the blue light by an output in 8, the white light by an output in 12, and the green light by an output in 16. The output functions are $F_r = a'bxy$, $F_w = ab'xy$, $F_b = ab'x'y$, and

$F_g = a'bx'y$. The control functions for relays X and Y are $F_x = ab'y' + (a + b)x$ and $F_y = ab + (a + b)y$. The corresponding circuit is left to the reader.

EXAMPLE 2. An electric combination lock is to be designed based on five visible keys A, B, C, D, and E and two hidden keys F and G. A solenoid is to withdraw the bolt when keys $B\,E\,A\,D$ are pressed consecutively, in that order only. (The solenoid is operated by current through its winding.) A burglar alarm is to sound if any error is made in manipulation of the keys. Key F is to shut off the alarm and release all secondary relays. Key G is to reset the lock.

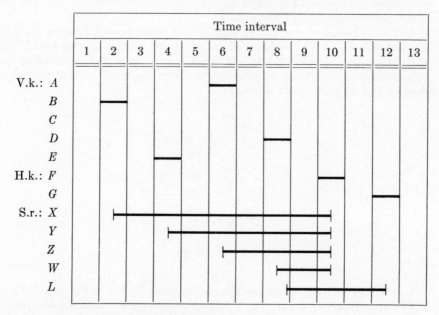

FIG. 5-39. Sequence diagram for the combination lock of Example 2. V.k. and H. k. denote visible and hidden keys.

Solution. First we will arrange two relays, T to operate the alarm, and L to operate the solenoid which releases the lock. This is done through make contacts on the relays. The reason for using relays here is that they permit locking paths to be introduced to maintain operation until the appropriate key is depressed to cause release of these devices. Figure 5-39 shows the correct operating sequence for operation of L and all secondary relays needed, except the one used to control the alarm. The latter cannot be shown without drawing all incorrect sequences as well.

The control functions are then given by

$$F_x = b + f'x, \qquad F_y = e + f'y, \qquad F_z = a + f'z,$$
$$F_w = d + f'w, \qquad F_l = xyzwt' + g'l.$$

Here the t' in the control function for L guarantees that the lock bolt will never be withdrawn if the alarm is sounding. Finally, the alarm relay T is controlled by

$$F_t = c + x'y + y'z + z'w + f't.$$

Note that the alarm will ring in case an error of any type is made. From these functions, the circuit can be readily drawn. This is left to the reader.

<h2 style="text-align:center">Exercises</h2>

1. Draw the circuit for Example 1.

2. Draw the circuit for Example 2.

3. Three brushes are to pick up signals from contacts on a rotating shaft as illustrated in Fig. 5–40. Design a circuit which will turn on a green light if the shaft is rotating in one direction and a red light if the shaft is rotating in the opposite direction. (It will be sufficient to design the circuit so that the lights flash on and off as the shaft rotates.)

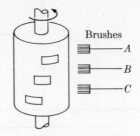

FIGURE 5–40

4. A model railroad layout has the configuration shown in Fig. 5–41. Each switch is controled by a solenoid. When the solenoid is not operated, the switch aligns on the straight section of track, and when the solenoid is operated, the switch connects the curved section to the straight section. Design a relay circuit that will cause the train to travel loop 1 first, then loop 2, then loop 3, and repeat indefinitely. The control is to be effected through keys at points A, B, and C, which will be operated by the passage of the train.

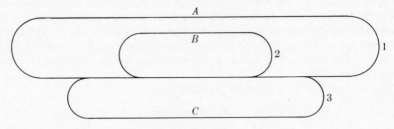

FIGURE 5–41

CHAPTER 6

CIRCUITS FOR ARITHMETIC COMPUTATION

6–1 Introduction. One of the most highly publicized achievements of the past few years has been the development of high-speed digital computers, often mistakenly referred to as electronic "brains." Although it is not our purpose to give a detailed description of the design or operation of such computers, it is appropriate to conclude the discussion on the algebra of circuits with specific mention of some of the circuit-design problems which arise in their construction. Among the features of a computer which must be designed are devices by which information and instructions can be given to the machine, devices by which the machine can carry out these instructions and perform a variety of specialized tasks, and devices by which the results of the machine's efforts can be made available to the operator. Each of these areas has its own special types of circuit-design problems. The second area is the one which is probably of most interest to the novice. For this reason, we have included this chapter on some of the basic circuits capable of performing the simple arithmetic operations of addition, subtraction, and multiplication. It is hoped that these few brief sections will stimulate the reader to pursue the subject further in one of the several available books which treat computer design in considerable detail.

Before we can design circuits that can compute with numbers, it is necessary to discuss ways in which numbers may be represented by circuit elements. Any such method depends, in turn, upon some coding scheme for designating numbers. Many different coding methods are employed, but probably the simplest one of all to understand is based upon the *binary* number system. The next section introduces this system.

6–2 The binary number system. The decimal number system is familiar to every reader and will be used to illustrate the meaning of the binary system. When we write the number 3814, each of the digits 3, 8, 1, and 4 conveys a meaning dependent on its position within the number: 3 refers to thousands, 8 to hundreds, 1 to tens, and 4 to units. Another way of conveying the same information is to write the number as a sum of multiples of powers of 10. Here we have

$$3814 = 3(10^3) + 8(10^2) + 1(10^1) + 4(10^0).$$

Having written 3814 in this way, we can easily observe the significance of 10 in our decimal system. The number 10 is referred to as the *radix* of the decimal system.

135

Any positive integer greater than 1 could serve as a radix as well as the integer 10. For instance, the number 194 written in radix 5 would read 1234, meaning that

$$194 = 1(5^3) + 2(5^2) + 3(5^1) + 4(5^0).$$

The same number in radix 7 would read 365, meaning $3(7^2) + 6(7^1) + 5(7^0)$. If a radix larger than 10 were used, it would be necessary to create some new symbols, since in any system, an integer smaller than the radix should be represented by a single digit.

To make the ideas just introduced more precise, we will define a *digit* to be any single symbol used to represent a nonnegative integer. A *number* is defined to be a symbol consisting of a sequence of $k + 1$ digits, $N = a_k \cdots a_2 a_1 a_0$, where each a_i is a digit. A number is related to the radix R of the number system by the equation

$$N = a_k R^k + \cdots + a_2 R^2 + a_1 R + a_0.$$

To convert any number N from the decimal system to the system with radix R, the following method will serve.

1. Determine the highest power, k, of R which does not exceed N.
2. Divide N by R^k. The quotient, a_k, is the first digit of N and the remainder, r_1, is used in step 3.
3. (a) If r_1 is larger than R^{k-1}, divide r_1 by R^{k-1} to obtain a quotient a_{k-1}, the second digit of N, and a remainder r_2 to be used in step 4.

(b) If r_1 is smaller than R^{k-1}, the second digit of N is 0, and r_1 is used in step 4.

4. Repeat step 3 with the result of (a) or (b) and continue until all powers of R less than k have been used.

EXAMPLE 1. Convert 97 to the number system with radix 3.

Solution. 3^4 equals 81 and is the highest power of 3 less than 97. $97 \div 81$ is 1 with remainder 16. The first digit of 97 in radix 3 is therefore 1. Now since $3^3 = 27$ is larger than 16, the second digit is 0. Next, 16 is divided by $3^2 = 9$ to give a quotient 1 and remainder 7. Thus the third digit is 1. Next, 7 is divided by 3 to give the quotient 2, the fourth digit, and remainder 1. Division by $3^0 = 1$ gives a quotient 1, the last digit of our number. Thus we find that the decimal number 97 should be written as 10,121 in the number system with radix 3.

To change from a given radix to the decimal system, it is necessary only to expand according to the definition in terms of powers of the radix and evaluate the resulting sum as a number in decimal notation.

EXAMPLE 2. Find the decimal equivalent of 2312 in the system of radix 4.

Solution. 2312 in radix 4 means

$$2(4^3) + 3(4^2) + 1(4) + 2 = 128 + 48 + 4 + 2,$$

which is equal to 182 in decimal notation.

The radix 2 is of special interest since a number written in radix 2 contains only two digits, 0 and 1. It is easy to see how such a number can be represented by a sequence of switches, lights, relays, or other devices, each of which has two states corresponding to 0 and 1. The system using radix 2 is called the *binary number system.* The general discussion above will serve to define radix 2 but, for convenience, Table 6–1 is included to show the first sixteen numbers in both the decimal system and the binary system. For conversion of an arbitrary number from the binary system to the decimal, or from the decimal to the binary, the methods above may be used.

TABLE 6–1

BINARY AND DECIMAL REPRESENTATIONS OF NUMBERS

Decimal	Binary	Decimal	Binary
1	1	9	1,001
2	10	10	1,010
3	11	11	1,011
4	100	12	1,100
5	101	13	1,101
6	110	14	1,110
7	111	15	1,111
8	1,000	16	10,000

Fractions may also be introduced in the binary system by considering negative powers of 2 and separating the number by a period at the appropriate place exactly as is done in the decimal system. We will limit the discussion in this chapter to whole numbers for the sake of simplicity, but no great difficulty is added with the inclusion of fractions. As an illustration, $\frac{3}{4}$ in decimal notation is 0.75, which means $7(10^{-1}) + 5(10^{-2})$. In the binary system, $\frac{3}{4}$ is written as 0.11, meaning $1(2^{-1}) + 1(2^{-2})$.

EXERCISES

1. Convert the decimal number 317 to the number system with

(a) radix 2   (b) radix 3   (c) radix 5

(d) radix 7   (e) radix 8   (f) radix 9

2. Convert the binary number 101,101 to the number system with

(a) radix 10   (b) radix 5   (c) radix 3   (d) radix 8

3. If 34,123 is a number in the system of radix 5, find its decimal equivalent.

4. Place each of the following in binary notation.

(a) 32   (b) 76   (c) 125   (d) 1024   (e) 1/16   (f) 1516

5. Change the following binary numbers to the decimal system.

(a) 101,111   (b) 111,101   (c) 100,001
(d) 10,110,101   (e) 11.01   (f) 1,111.11

6. Convert each of the following decimals into the binary system, giving your answers to six significant digits.

(a) 13.25   (b) 32.5   (c) 3.171   (d) 0.015

7. If t and e are understood to be digits representing ten and eleven, respectively, convert the number $2t,e76$ in radix 12 to an equivalent decimal.

8. Using t and e as in Exercise 7, convert the decimal 1276 to radix 12.

9. Find the sum and the product of 17 and 43 by first converting each to radix 5, then performing the operation, and finally converting back to the decimal system. Check your answers by the usual method.

10. Given $a = 10,110$ and $b = 111,001$, both in the binary system. Find, by using binary notation throughout, $a + b$, $b - a$, ab, and b/a, and then check your answers by converting to the decimal system.

6–3 Logical circuit elements. We have already introduced two devices which can be connected into circuits for useful purposes, namely, relays and manual switches. In the construction of electronic computers, other devices are more frequently used. Circuit elements involving diodes or vacuum tubes are very common. Rather than discuss the many types of electronic apparatus that may be used, we will introduce the idea of a *logical circuit element*. It will be enough to know that these elements can be constructed; in fact, commercially packaged elements of these types, suitable for use in many types of equipment, can be purchased directly. Whether these elements are constructed from relays or tubes, or other basic parts, will be immaterial in most of this chapter. The student may think in terms of relays, since, as we will show, it is possible to construct all the logical elements from relays alone. Often these relay circuits have very poor operating characteristics in comparison with circuits involving other components, but we will leave the discussion of electronic components to more advanced texts on computer design.

We will conceive of a logical circuit element as a little box or package with one or more input leads (wire connections) and one or more output leads. These leads will carry signals in the form of positive voltage corresponding to a value 1, or zero voltage corresponding to a value 0. We will use a single letter, say x, to stand for the condition of the lead. When the lead carries a signal, we will say that x takes on the value 1. When the lead does not carry a signal, we say that x has the value 0. This represents only a slight modification of our earlier point of view, where 1 and 0 meant closed or open circuits, since we can think of a closed circuit as one carrying a signal, and of an open circuit as one incapable of carrying a signal. Other signals than that of a positive voltage could be used equally well, and in fact the signal used will in general depend on the type of components used in circuit construction. We will use just this one type of signal for simplicity, and we will adapt all our circuits to its use.

We will diagram a circuit element as a circle with a letter inside to designate the type of element, and with lines indicating inputs and outputs. Arrows on these lines will indicate the difference between input and output, an arrow pointing toward the circle being used on each input.

The first logical circuit element we will consider has a single input and a single output. The function of this element is to obtain the complement of a given signal; that is, the output is 0 when the input is 1, and conversely. Figure 6–1 shows the notation we will use, a circle with C in the center, and one possible construction for this element in terms of relays. The input is designated x, so the output is x'.

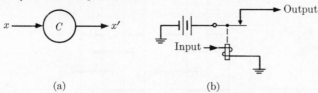

(a)   (b)

FIG. 6–1.   (a) Symbolic notation and (b) circuit for a complement.

The next two logical circuit elements correspond to the logical connections "and" and "or." Each may have two or more inputs and only a single output. The "and" element is shown in diagrams as a circle with A in the center. This element produces an output signal (output has value 1) if and only if every input carries a signal (has value 1). If the inputs to an "and" element are x, y, and z, for example, the output function may be written as xyz, where the notation is that of Boolean algebra. The "or" element, represented graphically by a circle with O in the center, produces an output signal whenever one or more inputs carry a signal. If the inputs to an "or" element are x, y, and z, for example, the output is the Boolean function $x + y + z$. Figure 6–2 shows the symbolic notations for these elements and possible circuits to realize the elements. Each is shown with only two inputs; the extension to more inputs is self-evident. Many other circuits, with these or other components, are possible.

A final logical circuit element will be termed a *flip-flop* and designated by a circle with an F in the center. This device has a single input and a

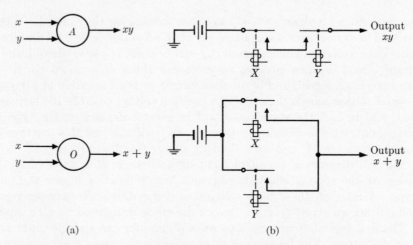

(a)   (b)

FIG. 6–2.   "And" and "or" logical circuit elements.

	Time interval								
	1	2	3	4	5	6	7	8	9
Input: A									
Secondary Relays: X									
Y									
Output									

FIG. 6–3.   Sequence chart for a flip-flop.

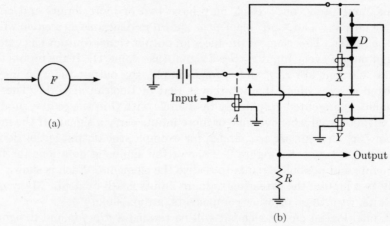

(a)

(b)

FIG. 6–4.   (a) Symbolic notation and (b) circuit for a flip-flop.

single output. It has two stable states, in one of which the output is 1, in the other of which the output is 0. The state of the flip-flop changes each time a signal appears (even momentarily) on the input lead, whereupon it maintains the new state and corresponding output until the next signal is received.

We will design a flip-flop by the methods of Chapter 5. The sequence chart of Fig. 6–3 represents the desired output in terms of input signals that occur intermittently. A choice of operating sequence for two secondary relays, sufficient to give the desired output, is also shown. The control functions for X and Y are: $F_x = ay' + a'x$ and $F_y = a'x + ay$. The output function is $ay' + a'x$, which is identical to F_x. Because these two functions are the same, the simplest way to get the desired output is directly from the control path of X, as shown in Fig. 6–4(b). A make contact on X could also be used (although this would cause a slight delay), giving an output sequence identical with the operate sequence of X. Either method would serve our purpose.

The flip-flop symbol to be used in future diagrams and the actual relay circuit that it represents are shown in Fig. 6–4. The symbol at D indicates a rectifying diode to prevent the sneak path which would otherwise cause Y to operate when A is operated and Y released. This flip-flop could be constructed more simply by using vacuum tubes.

EXERCISES

1. Draw the symbol and the circuit for the "and" circuit element with three inputs x, y, and z.

2. Draw the symbol and the circuit for the "or" element with three inputs x, y, and z.

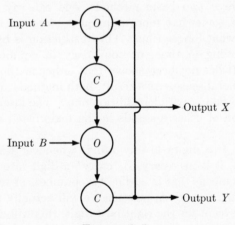

FIGURE 6–5

3. The diagram in Fig. 6–5 is that of a modified flip-flop having two outputs and two inputs. The outputs are complements of each other, and each output is much like the F flip-flop of the text. Show that when the outputs are $x = 0$, $y = 1$, a momentary signal on input B will cause outputs X and Y to reverse their states. [*Hint:* Tabulate the states of all leads before and after the signal at B.] Further show that when the outputs are $x = 1$, $y = 0$, a momentary signal on input A will cause outputs X and Y to reverse their states.

4. Draw the relay circuit for the flip-flop of Exercise 3, using the same notation for inputs and outputs.

6–4 Addition of binary numbers. There are several common methods by which computers add numbers. One thing peculiar to all computers is that numbers are added in pairs only. If a sum of three numbers is required, two numbers are summed first and the third is then added to the sum. In the following discussion, then, we will consider only the problem of adding two numbers. Methods for addition may be classified as either *parallel* or *serial* methods. The difference in method is determined by the way in which the numbers are transmitted or fed into the computer.

In *parallel* methods, a number is given by signals (or lack of them) carried by a set of leads, one for each digit of the number. The number 101, for instance, would be represented by three leads, the first and third of which would carry a signal (positive voltage) and the second of which would carry no signal. Parallel methods of addition will add two numbers by considering all positions in the numbers at once and producing on a third set of leads signals which correspond to the sum.

In *serial* methods, numbers are transmitted to the machine one digit at a time, beginning with the digit in lowest position. As the sequence of signals is fed into the adding device, the digits are combined progressively and the sum is given as a sequential output.

Concerning these two basic methods, one can say that the parallel method requires somewhat more apparatus, whereas the serial method requires a somewhat longer time. This distinction is by no means clear-cut, and the saving in time, or conversely in equipment, depends on many factors. It has not been shown that either method is definitely the better in any general sense. As a result, both methods are being used. We will discuss a method of parallel addition only. The interested student can find a description of other methods in the texts listed at the end of this chapter.

In combining two digits in any radix, whenever the sum exceeds or equals the radix, it is necessary to "carry" a digit into the next position to the left. This means that in adding two numbers of several digits, there will be times when in a given position we will actually need to add three digits. In fact, except for the rightmost digit, this will always be the case since we will always consider a carry digit which may be either 0 or 1 in the binary system. Because of this carry, it is convenient to perform additions in two steps. The first step will be performed by a new logical circuit element which we will term a *half adder*. The half adder will be a device capable of performing the operation indicated by Table 6–2. That

TABLE 6–2

ADDITION OF BINARY NUMBERS

First addend	0	1	0	1
Second addend	0	0	1	1
Sum digit	0	1	1	0
Carry digit	0	0	0	1

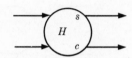

FIG. 6–6. Symbolic notation for a half adder.

is, the half adder will have two inputs, corresponding to the two addends, and it will have two outputs, one giving the sum digit and the other giving the carry digit, as indicated in the table. The symbol to be used in future circuit diagrams is shown in Fig. 6–6. The lower case letters s and c are used to distinguish between the two outputs.

A circuit for the half adder can be derived readily by considering the sum and carry outputs separately as functions of the inputs. Suppose that we call the inputs x and y; then it is clear that the function for the sum may be written as $s = xy' + x'y$ since 1 appears as the sum if and only if one, but not both, of the addends is 1. Similarly, the function for the carry is given by $c = xy$. Interpreting these functions directly in terms of logical elements, we have one circuit for a half adder as shown in Fig. 6–7. Other circuits are suggested in the exercises.

With the half adder of Fig. 6–7 as a component, it is not difficult to build a circuit for parallel addition of two binary numbers. Let us assume for simplicity that the two numbers are each 3-digit (or less), represented by

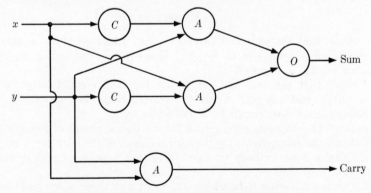

FIG. 6–7. Logical circuit for a half adder.

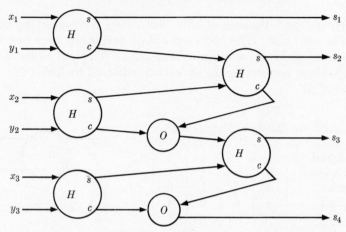

FIG. 6–8. Circuit for the addition of two 3-digit numbers.

$X = x_3 x_2 x_1$ and $Y = y_3 y_2 y_1$, where each x_i and y_j is either 0 or 1. These digits are supplied in pairs to half adders as shown in Fig. 6–8. The sum (answer) is the number $s_4 s_3 s_2 s_1$, given by the four outputs. That this circuit will work is self-evident. After the first position, the circuit is the same for each higher position. Two inputs, say x_2 and y_2, are combined in a half adder, with the sum going to a second half adder to be combined with a carry from position 1. The sum of half adder 2 is the second digit of the answer, and the carry from the two half adders are combined with an "or" element to give the carry for the next higher position. Note that these two half adders cannot both yield a carry signal, since if the first showed 1 as a carry it must have 0 as a sum and hence the second half adder cannot also have a carry. If more than three digits are being added, the bottom output becomes the carry to the fourth position rather than the fourth digit of the answer.

EXERCISES

1. Show that the sum and carry of a half adder could be written as $s = (x + y)(x' + y')$ and $c = (x' + y')'$. Draw the corresponding logical circuit diagram similar to Fig. 6–7.

2. Show that the sum and carry of a half adder could be given by $s = (x + y)(xy)'$ and $c = xy$. Draw the corresponding logical circuit. (This is probably the simplest circuit for a half adder.)

3. Draw the complete relay circuit for the logical circuit of Fig. 6–7.

4. Draw the relay circuit for the logical circuit of Exercise 2.

5. Draw a logical circuit similar to Fig. 6–8 capable of adding two 5-digit numbers.

6. Define a *full adder* to be a logical element with three inputs and two outputs as follows. Two inputs shall be the nth digits of the two addends, and the third

input shall be the carry digit from the adder used in combining the $(n - 1)$st digits of the addends. The outputs shall be the sum and carry digits for the nth place. First make a table showing the eight possible combinations of inputs and the desired outputs. Then write the corresponding Boolean functions which will give the desired outputs, and finally draw the logical circuit for the full adder.

7. Draw a logical circuit, using the full adder designed in Exercise 6, which will add two 3-digit binary numbers.

6–5 Subtraction of binary numbers. The design of a circuit for subtraction is very similar to the problem of design for addition. The differences are primarily that the inputs must be distinguished as to order and, instead of a carry signal, it is necessary to indicate a borrow signal. Table 6–3 indicates the operation which must be performed by a circuit element we will term a *half subtracter*. The symbolic notation to be used in circuit diagrams is given in Fig. 6–9. We must distinguish between the two inputs. The plus sign will denote the minuend digit, and the minus sign will denote the digit from the subtrahend. The outputs will show the difference digit and the borrow digit.

TABLE 6–3

SUBTRACTION OF BINARY NUMBERS

Minuend digit	0	1	0	1
Subtrahend digit	0	0	1	1
Difference digit	0	1	1	0
Borrow digit	0	0	1	0

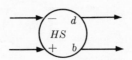

FIG. 6–9. Symbolic notation for a half subtracter.

To design a half subtracter, we note by consulting Table 6–3 that the function representing the difference output is given by $d = xy' + x'y$ if x and y represent the two inputs. The order of the inputs is immaterial for the difference output, but to determine the borrow output an order must be stated. We will specify x as minuend digit and y as subtrahend digit. Then the borrow output is given by $b = x'y$. From these functions, the half subtracter can be designed immediately, as shown in Fig. 6–10. Note that the circuit for the difference in a half subtracter is identical to the circuit for the sum in a half adder.

Now, using the half subtracter and the "or" element just as was done in the preceding section on addition, a logical circuit can be designed which will subtract two binary numbers. We will let the minuend be a 3-digit number $X = x_3x_2x_1$. (The restriction to three digits is only for simplicity of illustration. Any number of digits can be handled in the same way.) The subtrahend $Y = y_3y_2y_1$ will be a number of not more than three digits, which we will assume does not exceed the minuend in size. The difference of the two digits is given as the number $D = d_3d_2d_1$, repre-

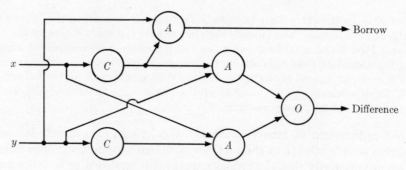

FIG. 6–10.   Logical circuit for a half subtracter.

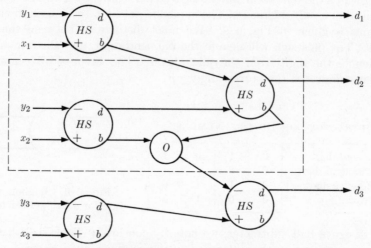

FIG. 6–11.   Circuit for the subtraction of two 3-digit numbers.

sented by the outputs of the circuit. The diagram is given in Fig. 6–11. The unit which combines the second digits is the typical unit. This part of the circuit is enclosed in a broken line. If larger numbers are to be combined, this portion of the diagram is repeated for all number positions except the first and last, which are modified as in the diagram for 3-digit numbers.

EXERCISES

1. Find another pair of functions which will represent the outputs of a half subtracter, and use these as a basis for a logical circuit diagram. (See Exercises 1 and 2 of Section 6–4.)

2. Draw the complete relay circuit for the logical circuit of Exercise 1.

3. Draw a logical circuit similar to Fig. 6–11 capable of subtracting two 5-digit numbers.

4. Let a *full subtracter* denote a circuit element which receives the nth digits of the subtrahend and minuend and the borrow signal from the $(n-1)$st digits as inputs, and which gives for its outputs the nth difference digit and borrow digit. First construct a table showing the eight possible input combinations and the desired outputs. Then write the Boolean functions for the outputs, and finally draw the logical circuit for a full subtracter.

5. Draw a logical circuit, using the full subtracter of Exercise 4, which will subtract two 3-digit binary numbers.

6–6 Accumulation. One very important operation that can be performed on a calculator is that of accumulation. Accumulation is nothing more than repeated addition (or subtraction). Instead of receiving two numbers as inputs and producing a third as an output, the *accumulator* accepts numbers one at a time. As each number is received, the accumulator adds it to the number already stored and then stores the sum. In the process, the original numbers are erased and only the sum remains. Because of the necessity for storing a number, then changing it to a new number which is again stored, it is reasonably obvious that the flip-flop will be a basic element in an accumulator.

The *accumulator register* will be a sequence of flip-flops, one of which will correspond to each digit of the number stored. This register will have a number stored in it at the beginning of the operation we are considering. (This could, of course, be the number zero.) The addend, which is to be added to the number stored in the accumulator, will be a number stored on a second sequence of flip-flops constituting the *addend register*. We will design an accumulator in units by thinking separately of each part of the circuit which involves a given digit only, say the nth digit, of the numbers involved. This part of the circuit, or unit, will be repeated for each digit, with the exception of the first and last digits, where minor modifications are required.

The function of the nth unit of the accumulator is represented in Table 6–4. The inputs for this unit consist of the signals from the accumulator register, addend register, and the carry from the preceding unit. The outputs consist of a carry to the next higher position and, for convenience, the complement of this carry, which we will call *noncarry* and designate by n or c', and finally a pulse which may or may not be applied to the accumulator. When necessary, this pulse changes the state of the accumulator digit to represent the new sum, which will be stored following the addition operation. The inputs and outputs of this unit are shown schematically in Fig. 6–12.

The major difficulty is that this cannot be a combinational circuit. The nature of the flip-flop in the accumulator makes it necessary for the circuit to be sequential. It will be convenient, circuitwise, to perform the computations for carry before that for sum. The reason is that the carry output

TABLE 6–4

FUNCTION OF AN ACCUMULATOR UNIT

Inputs			Outputs		
Accumulator register y	Addend register x	Carry c	Add pulse p	Carry c	Noncarry $n = c'$
1	1	1	0	1	0
1	1	0	1	1	0
1	0	1	1	1	0
1	0	0	0	0	1
0	1	1	0	1	0
0	1	0	1	0	1
0	0	1	1	0	1
0	0	0	0	0	1

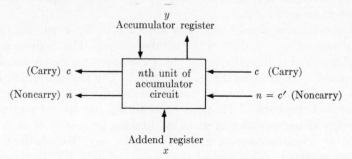

y
Accumulator register

(Carry) c ← nth unit of   ← c (Carry)
                      accumulator
(Noncarry) n ←   circuit   ← $n = c'$ (Noncarry)

Addend register
x

FIG. 6–12. Block diagram of an accumulator unit.

depends on the carry input, the addend register, and the accumulator register as it was before the addition. If the pulse to the accumulator were supplied before the carry output is established, an erroneous result would be obtained. The method which we will use (and this is only one of many) is carried out in the following steps.

1. Addend is supplied to addend register.
2. Signal is supplied to noncarry input of the lowest-order digit.
3. After all carry outputs are stable, an "add pulse" is supplied simultaneously to each unit.

Step 1 is self-explanatory, and merely supplies the required addend inputs as steady signals. Now a signal is applied to noncarry at the lowest order to start the propagation of carry signals throughout the circuit. The circuit should be such that each unit in turn, from lowest to highest order,

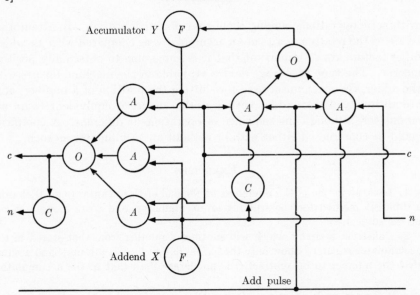

FIG. 6–13. Logical circuit for the nth unit of a binary accumulator.

will stabilize with proper carry-signal outputs. The circuit for the pulse to the accumulator must be such that nothing happens until all carry outputs have been formed. This is accomplished by supplying a pulse, termed an *add pulse* and designated p, to each unit after the carry signal has passed through all units. The proper timing can be determined from the carry signals, since they are paired so that one or the other will always produce a signal. When the carry reaches the highest-order unit, the add-pulse signal is given, causing the new sum to appear in the accumulator register.

From Table 6–4, the functions for the outputs of a unit can be readily computed as follows.

Output to accumulator: $f = (x'c + xc')p$. Here p is the add pulse mentioned in the preceding paragraph.

Carry output: $c = xy + yc + xc$. Here c on the left side of the equation refers to output carry, and on the right to input carry.

Noncarry output: $n = (xy + yc + xc)'$. Since this signal is the negative of the preceding, it can be obtained through a single "complement" element.

The logical circuit for the nth unit is shown in Fig. 6–13. This accumulator, or any of the many circuits which accomplish the same result, is of great value in a computer. In addition to its obvious use for summing sets of addends, it can be employed to advantage in many more complicated arithmetic operations, among them that of multiplication. In attempting to assess the relative merits of an accumulator as compared with an adder, other factors are so important that it is impossible to obtain any positive answer. The type of storage device available in the machine for use with the adder, the mechanism used for shifting the position of a number, etc., are all involved. An adder with a storing device is equivalent to an accumulator, although the sequence of operations is different. A computer could be constructed either with or without an accumulator as such.

EXERCISES

1. Look up in one of the references at the end of this chapter (e.g., Richards) a different method for constructing an accumulator, and write a short report on the subject.

2. Construct a circuit which will subtract a number from that stored in the accumulator register. Show only the logical design for the nth unit, and assume that the number to be subtracted is not larger than that in the accumulator.

6–7 Binary multiplication. It has been mentioned in the other sections on arithmetic operations that many other logical circuits are known and used for each of the operations discussed. This situation is even more pronounced with respect to multiplication. Since the process itself is more complicated, it is only reasonable that more variations exist for multiplication. Among the many methods, the most frequently used are those which employ the use of an accumulator in one way or another. The following binary multiplication problem illustrates the steps which must be performed by the computer:

$$
\begin{array}{r}
111 \\
101 \\
\hline
111 \\
000 \\
111 \\
\hline
100011.
\end{array}
$$

The partial products are easy to obtain since they are each either zero or identical to the multiplicand. However, the addition is complicated because the partial products to be accumulated are not simply 3-digit numbers since each successive partial product is shifted one position to the left of the partial product above it. Besides accumulation, then, it is necessary to include a shifting device capable of reproducing the multiplicand in any desired position. The shifting may be done either upon the partial products or upon the number in the accumulator itself, just as long as the digits are aligned properly before each step in the computation.

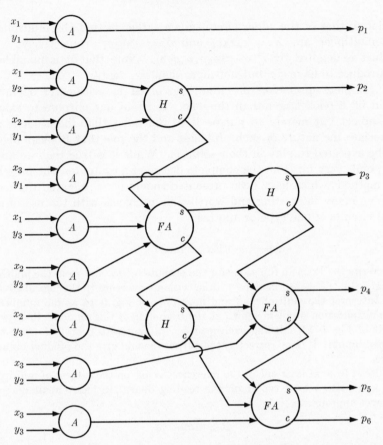

FIG. 6–14. Logical circuit for the simultaneous multiplication of two 3-digit numbers.

The preceding discussion has indicated a way in which the problem of multiplication can be, and usually is, approached. However, rather than introduce the shifting circuits necessary for this approach, we will conclude this chapter with a circuit capable of multiplying two 3-digit numbers directly. This circuit (Fig. 6–14) depends only on logical elements already introduced. Although the circuit is by no means trivially self-evident, a careful consideration of the various paths in connection with the sample problem above should convince the student of the validity of the circuit. The half adder is used with the notation introduced earlier and, in addition, the full adder described in Exercise 6, Section 6–4, is used with identical notation except that FA replaces the letter H found in a half adder. The two elements perform in the same way except that a full adder accepts three inputs instead of two. The notation for this circuit is similar to that of the adder circuit given earlier in that the multiplicand and multiplier are $X = x_3x_2x_1$ and $Y = y_3y_2y_1$, respectively. The product is denoted by $P = p_6p_5p_4p_3p_2p_1$. Note that it is possible for the product to have six, but not more than six, digits.

A complete discussion of circuits involved in arithmetic operations would fill a book larger than this one. It is not our purpose to exhaust the subject but merely to pursue it to the point that the student may appreciate the nature of such problems and the role that Boolean algebra can be expected to play in their solution. While it is true that we are, at this point, very far from the complete design of a computer, the principles and methods which have been presented should have prepared the reader to solve many interesting and worthwhile problems with the use of electrical circuits of one type or another.

EXERCISES

1. Write the Boolean functions for the outputs p_1, p_2, and p_3 in the multiplier of Fig. 6–14. (This can be done with or without reference to the logical circuit.)

2. Interpret the multiplicand and multiplier of Fig. 6–14 as the numbers of the multiplication problem shown at the beginning of this section. Redraw the circuit of Fig. 6–14, labeling each lead accordingly with 0 or 1 to correspond to these inputs. If done correctly, the outputs should give the product obtained before.

3. Read from at least one of the references below on the subject of multiplication, and write a brief report on the reading done. Include circuit diagrams wherever appropriate.

REFERENCES

BLANKENBAKER, J. V., How Computers do Arithmetic, *Control Engineering*, Vol. 3, no. 4 (April 1956).

BOOTH, A. D., and BOOTH, K. H. V., *Automatic Digital Calculators*, Butterworth Scientific Publications, London, 1953.

KEISTER, RITCHIE, and WASHBURN, *The Design of Switching Circuits*, D. Van Nostrand, 1951.

PHISTER, MONTGOMERY, JR., *Logical Design of Digital Computers*, John Wiley and Sons, 1958.

RICHARDS, R. K., *Arithmetic Operations in Digital Computers*, D. Van Nostrand, 1955.

Staff of Harvard Computation Laboratory, *Synthesis of Electronic Computing and Control Circuits*, Harvard University Press, 1951.

CHAPTER 7

INTRODUCTION TO PROBABILITY IN FINITE SAMPLE SPACES

7-1 Introduction. In Chapter 1, the algebra of sets was developed primarily as a means of introducing in an intuitive way the idea of a Boolean algebra. The applications of this algebra to "practical" problems was somewhat limited, and many of this type of problem were later solved with the algebra of logic. It might appear, then, that the algebra of sets has little to offer in its own right other than that it nicely illustrates the basic concepts of Boolean algebra. This could not be further from the truth. This chapter has been included in part to demonstrate the vital role played by the algebra of sets in mathematics.

There are many students who have been introduced to the subject of probability in elementary courses in such a way as to encourage the notion that probability is highly intuitive and not very precise from a mathematical standpoint. Working problems in probability often becomes little more than out-guessing the teacher. It is hoped that this brief introduction will clarify the notions of *probability*, *event*, and *sample space*, at least in the finite case. The finite case is sufficiently general to solve many problems arising in situations familiar to the student. For other cases and more involved problems, the reader is referred to the more extensive treatments listed in the bibliography.

7-2 Event, sample space, probability. Statements such as "It is likely to rain tomorrow," "A bridge hand is not apt to contain four aces," and "If you have five children, it is probable that one or more of them are boys" are probability statements. One of the purposes for studying probability is the desire to make such statements quantitative. For example, the statement "If I flip a coin, the chances that it will turn up heads is one-half" is a quantitative statement of probability which is usually accepted as valid. The procedure followed in making such quantitative statements is to construct a mathematical model which appears to represent the case in question, then to use the methods of mathematical probability theory to analyze the model, and finally to apply the results to the practical case. Probability theory is concerned with mathematical models rather than with natural problems. That is, the theory of probability does not deal specifically with natural phenomena, but rather with abstract mathematical concepts. Its usefulness depends upon the ability of the investigator to construct a model which reasonably reflects the actual situation.

Suppose that we consider either a real or a conceptual experiment with a finite number N of possible outcomes. We will take a universal set to be the set of all outcomes and for any subset X, we define the probability of X to be the number $P(X) = n(X)/N$. We note that this definition implies immediately that $P(1) = 1$, $P(0) = 0$, and $P(X') = 1 - P(X)$. In the language of probability, the universal set is referred to as the *sample space*, each subset is termed an *event*, and the unit sets are called *sample points*. $P(X)$ is the ratio of the number of sample points in the event X to the number of sample points in the sample space, and is usually referred to as the *probability of the occurrence of the event X*.

In the above definition, the words *experiment* and *outcome* have been used to make the concepts intuitively meaningful. It should be pointed out, however, that these concepts are not part of the mathematical model. The model consists solely of a set of N arbitrary elements, the possible subsets of this set, and the numbers $P(X)$ assigned to each subset X.

This model can be generalized in two ways, first by allowing a sample space with more than a finite number of distinct sample points, and also by assigning probabilities to sample points in an arbitrary manner, rather than requiring that each sample point have probability $1/N$. Both of these generalizations are included in the usual courses in probability theory. The purpose of this chapter is to present an insight into the role which the algebra of sets plays in the theory, and for this purpose it will be sufficient to consider only the simplest case, as stated in our definition.

As the preceding paragraphs have suggested, the problem of choosing a suitable model is often the most difficult step in the formulation of accurate probability statements. As an illustration of a correct and an incorrect method of making the choice, consider the problem of determining the probability of the occurrence of a sum of 7 in rolling two dice.

FIRST MODEL. Suppose that we consider the possible "outcomes" to be the eleven possible sums $2, 3, \ldots, 12$. That is, our sample space will have eleven points, and if X represents the event that a sum of 7 occurs, we have that $P(X) = \frac{1}{11}$. Intuition tells us that this answer is not "correct," and in fact it does not represent the actual probability. It is not the mathematics that is at fault, but rather the choice of model. There are two ways in which the model could be changed to give a more reasonable answer. One is to assign probabilities in a different manner. Clearly 7 is more probable than 2 or 12. Since our definition of probability will not allow this change, we will consider the second possibility.

SECOND MODEL. Let the sample space consist of thirty-six points, each corresponding to a pair of numbers selected from the integers $1, 2, \ldots, 6$. The first number of the pair will represent the face appearing on the first die, the second will represent the face appearing on the second die. Thus $(1, 1)$, $(2, 5)$, and $(5, 2)$ are each sample points. Again, let X be the event that 7 is the sum of the faces appearing on the two dice. X contains the six points $(1, 6)$, $(6, 1)$, $(2, 5)$, $(5, 2)$, $(3, 4)$, and $(4, 3)$. Hence $P(X) = \frac{6}{36} = \frac{1}{6}$, which is a more reasonable answer than the first.

Both answers are mathematically correct, since each was correctly derived from the model. The second is, of course, more realistic. In more complicated applications, it may be difficult, or even impossible, to determine whether a given model fits the application closely enough, although the fit of a model may usually be tested in many ways. In the example above, for instance, one might roll two dice again and again, say six hundred times. If the result showed approximately one hundred occurrences of 7 we would tend to believe that the second model was well chosen.

In stating problems on probability concerning two events X and Y, the phrase "the probability of occurrence of X or Y" means the probability of the event $X + Y$, and "the probability of occurrence of X and Y" means the probability of the event XY.

EXAMPLE 1. A bag contains ten tags numbered $0, 1, 2, \ldots, 9$. Let X be the event that a chance drawing results in 5 or 8, and Y be the event that a digit larger than 5 is drawn. Find the probabilities that (a) event X occurs, (b) event Y occurs, (c) event X or event Y occurs, and (d) event X and event Y occur.

Solution. The sample space contains 10 points, X contains 2 points, Y contains 4 points, $X + Y$ contains 5 points, and XY contains 1 point. The probabilities are therefore:

(a) $P(X) = \frac{1}{5}$,   (b) $P(Y) = \frac{2}{5}$,

(c) $P(X + Y) = \frac{1}{2}$,   (d) $P(XY) = \frac{1}{10}$.

The following two theorems are direct consequences of theorems in Chapter 1 and are useful in considering probabilities of combinations of events. We will say that two events are *mutually exclusive* in case the sets with which the events correspond are disjoint. Intuitively, mutually exclusive events are events which cannot occur simultaneously.

THEOREM 1. If A and B are mutually exclusive events, then $P(AB) = 0$ and $P(A + B) = P(A) + P(B)$.

Proof. That $P(AB) = 0$ follows immediately from the definition of the phrase *mutually disjoint*.

Since A and B represent disjoint sets, it follows from Section 1–10 that $n(A + B) = n(A) + n(B)$, and dividing both sides by N (the number of elements in the sample space), we have that $P(A + B) = P(A) + P(B)$.

THEOREM 2. For arbitrary events A and B, $P(A + B) = P(A) + P(B) - P(AB)$.

Proof. If the sample space in which events A and B occur contains N elements, then by definition, $P(A + B) = n(A + B)/N$. By Theorem 1 of Section 1–10, $n(A + B) = n(A) + n(B) - n(AB)$, and therefore

$$P(A + B) = \frac{n(A)}{N} + \frac{n(B)}{N} - \frac{n(AB)}{N}$$
$$= P(A) + P(B) - P(AB),$$

which completes the proof.

EXAMPLE 2. Given that $P(A) = \frac{1}{2}$, $P(B) = \frac{2}{3}$, and $P(AB) = \frac{2}{9}$ for two events A and B, find (a) $P(A + B)$, (b) $P(A'B')$, and (c) $P(A'B)$.

Solution. (a) By Theorem 2, $P(A + B) = P(A) + P(B) - P(AB) = \frac{1}{2} + \frac{2}{3} - \frac{2}{9} = \frac{17}{18}$. (b) $A'B'$ is the complement of $A + B$, so $P(A'B') = 1 - P(A + B) = \frac{1}{18}$. (c) Since $B = B(A + A') = AB + A'B$ and the sets AB and $A'B$ are disjoint, $P(B) = P(AB) + P(A'B)$, or $P(A'B) = P(B) - P(AB) = \frac{2}{3} - \frac{2}{9} = \frac{4}{9}$.

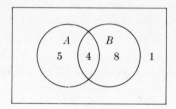

FIG. 7–1.   Numbered Venn diagram for Example 2.

It is often convenient to draw a Venn diagram in connection with a probability problem as an aid to visualizing the relationship between events. Figure 7–1 shows a Venn diagram for Example 2. The various regions may be numbered exactly as was done in Section 1–10. The number of elements selected for the universal set is arbitrary except that it should be a multiple of each denominator of the given probabilities so that all numbers are integral. In the present case, 18 will serve as the number of elements in the universal set (or sample space). From this and the given probabilities, we get that $n(A) = 9$, $n(B) = 12$, and $n(AB) = 4$. The remaining numbers can be supplied as usual. From the numbered diagram, any desired probability can be read off by inspection.

EXERCISES

1. A bowl contains five tags numbered 1, 2, 3, 4, and 5. One drawing is made, and then, without replacing the first tag, a second drawing is made. Describe the mathematical model used, and determine the following probabilities.

(a) The probability that the first tag is an even number.

(b) The probability that the second tag is even.

(c) The probability that both tags are even.

(d) The probability that either the first or the second tag is even.

2. Referring to Exercise 4 of Section 1–10, what is the probability that a person chosen at random

(a) has no tag?

(b) has exactly one color of tag?

(c) has a red or a blue tag or both?

(d) has a blue tag but not a white tag?

(e) has tags of more than one color?

3. Two dice are thrown. Let A be the event that the sum of the faces is even, and B be the event that at least one die shows a 5. Describe the model used and find the probabilities of the following events.

(a) A (b) B (c) $A + B$ (d) AB (e) $A'B$ (f) $AB + A'B'$

4. A set of double-six dominoes consists of small blocks of wood, each block having a number of spots from 0 to 6 inclusive stamped on each end. The two ends are exactly alike (other than perhaps the number of spots), no two dominoes are identical, and there are 28 of them in the set. Find the probability that a domino drawn at random from such a set

(a) has a 5 on one end or both,

(b) has no digit larger than 3 on either end,

(c) has an odd digit on both ends,

(d) has a total number of spots equal to seven.

5. A and B are events in a certain sample space. It is given that $P(A) = \frac{1}{2}$, $P(B) = \frac{2}{3}$, and $P(A + B) = \frac{3}{4}$. Find

(a) $P(AB)$ (b) $P(A' + B')$ (c) $P(A'B)$ (d) $P(A + B')$

6. Theorem 2 is a direct extension of Theorem 1 of Section 1–10. State and prove a probability theorem which extends the corollary of the latter in the same way.

7. Three events A, B, and C in a certain sample space have the following properties: $P(A) = 0.35$, $P(B) = 0.60$, $P(C) = 0.45$, $P(AB) = 0.25$, $P(AC) = 0.15$, $P(BC) = 0.20$, and $P(ABC) = 0.10$. Find

(a) $P(A + B)$ (b) $P(A + C)$ (c) $P(A + B + C)$

(d) $P(A'BC)$ (e) $P(AB'C')$ (f) $P(A + B' + C)$

(g) the probability that one and only one of the events A, B, C occurs.

(h) the probability that exactly two of the events A, B, C occur.

7–3 Conditional probability. To introduce the concept of conditional probability, consider the following example. An urn contains 10 large marbles of which 6 are white and 4 are black, and 10 small marbles of which 3 are white and 7 are black. Let the event that a marble drawn at random is white be denoted by W, and that it is large be denoted by L.

It is clear that $P(W) = \frac{9}{20}$. Suppose that a marble is drawn and it is large. The probability that it is also white is $\frac{3}{5}$. The reason these values are different is that the first is based on a sample space with 20 points of which 9 correspond to white marbles, and the second is based on a sample space of 10 points of which 6 correspond to white marbles. The second probability will be referred to as the probability that the ball is white knowing it is large, and will be denoted by $P(W|L)$. This intuitive example suggests the following definition.

DEFINITION. Let X be an event in an arbitrary sample space with nonzero probability, and let Y be any event in the same sample space. The *conditional probability* that Y occurs knowing that X has occurred is defined by

$$P(Y|X) = \frac{n(XY)}{n(X)}. \tag{1}$$

If both numerator and denominator of $P(Y|X)$ are divided by the number of points in the sample space, this formula becomes

$$P(Y|X) = \frac{P(XY)}{P(X)}. \tag{2}$$

Still another useful form for the formula is obtained by multiplying both sides of (2) by $P(X)$. This gives

$$P(XY) = P(Y|X)\,P(X). \tag{3}$$

A final formula which is often useful comes as an application of Theorem 2 of Section 1–10. Let Y be any event, and let $X_1, X_2, \ldots, X_m$ be events representing disjoint sets (mutually exclusive) and such that

$$X_1 + X_2 + \cdots + X_m = 1,$$

the entire sample space. Then it follows from Theorem 2 of Section 1–10 that $P(Y) = P(YX_1) + P(YX_2) + \cdots + P(YX_m)$, and applying (3) above, we obtain

$$P(Y) = P(Y|X_1)\,P(X_1) + P(Y|X_2)\,P(X_2) + \cdots$$
$$+ P(Y|X_m)\,P(X_m). \tag{4}$$

EXAMPLE 1. Find the probability that a card dealt from a bridge deck is an ace, if it is known to be either an ace or a face card (that is, A, K, Q, or J).

Solution. Let Y denote the event that the card is an ace, and X the event that it is either an ace or a face card. The definition gives

$$P(Y|X) = \frac{n(XY)}{n(X)} = \frac{4}{16} = \frac{1}{4}.$$

EXAMPLE 2. A certain group of students is two thirds males and one third females. Of these, one tenth of the males are color-blind. What is the probability that a student selected at random will be a color-blind male?

Solution. Let Y be the event that the student is color-blind, and X the event that he is male. Equation (3) gives

$$P(XY) = P(Y|X)\, P(X) = (\tfrac{1}{10})\, (\tfrac{2}{3}) = \tfrac{1}{15}.$$

EXAMPLE 3. In a factory, three operators A, B, and C alternate in shifts in operating a certain machine. Records show that the number of parts produced by A, B, and C, respectively, are in the ratio 4:5:6. Of the parts produced, 1% of A's, 2% of B's, and 3% of C's are defective. What is the probability that a part drawn at random from the output of their machine will be defective?

Solution. Let D represent the event that the part is defective, and let A, B, and C represent the events that the part is produced by operator A, B, or C, respectively. Using Eq. (4), we find that

$$P(D) = P(D|A)\, P(A) + P(D|B)\, P(B) + P(D|C)\, P(C)$$
$$= 0.01\ (\tfrac{4}{15}) + 0.02\ (\tfrac{1}{3}) + 0.03\ (\tfrac{2}{5})$$
$$= 0.0213, \quad \text{approximately.}$$

EXERCISES

1. If a die is thrown, find (a) the probability that it will come up 6 and (b) the probability that it will come up 6, knowing that it will come up 4 or more.

2. A die is rolled twice. Find the probability that the sum of faces is 7, knowing that 2 appeared on the first roll.

3. A student is selected at random from the students described in Exercise 2 of Section 1–10. (a) What is the probability that he takes math? (b) What is the probability that he takes math if it is known that he takes English? (c) What is the probability that he takes math if it is known that he takes English and chemistry?

4. An urn contains 15 marbles of which 10 are white and 5 are black. A marble is selected at random and is not replaced. Then a second is drawn. Use Eq. (3) to find the probability that both marbles are white.

5. Six urns contain 10 balls each. The first contains 1 white and 9 black balls, and in general, urn number i contains i white and $10 - i$ black balls, for $i = 1$, $2, \ldots, 6$. An urn is selected at random and, from it, a ball is drawn. Use Eq. (4) to find the probability that the ball is white.

6. If, in Exercise 5, a white ball is drawn and discarded, find the probability that the next ball drawn from the same urn is white.

7. A jar contains 15 red and 5 blue tags. A drawing is made, and the tag is returned to the jar with 5 more tags of the same color. Find the probability that a second drawing from the jar will be a red tag.

8. Given for two events A and B that $P(A) = \tfrac{1}{2}$, $P(B) = \tfrac{2}{3}$, and $P(A|B) = \tfrac{1}{3}$. Find (a) $P(A')$, (b) $P(AB)$, (c) $P(A + B)$, and (d) $P(B|A)$.

9. Three jars contain the following objects.

Jar 1 contains 5 tags numbered 1, 2, 3, 4, and 5.
Jar 2 contains 10 marbles of which 3 are white and 7 are black.
Jar 3 contains 10 marbles of which 5 are white and 5 are black.

A tag will be drawn at random from jar 1. If the number on the tag is even, a marble will be drawn at random from jar 2. If the number on the tag is odd, a marble will be drawn at random from jar 3. Find the probability that the resulting marble is white.

10. For two events A and B, it is known that the probability of the occurrence of A is twice that of B, and that $P(A|B)$ is $\frac{1}{2}$. Find $P(B|A)$.

7–4 Some aids to counting. The question of how one should proceed to count the number of elements in a set is not, strictly speaking, a part of the algebra of sets. However, to demonstrate how the algebra of sets forms the basis of probability theory, we would like to investigate sample spaces of a more involved nature. To do so requires the use of the theory of permutations and combinations. This theory is essentially a counting technique, and will be discussed briefly for the benefit of readers who may not have the necessary background. Anyone familiar with this material may easily proceed to Section 7–5.

First, we shall define an *ordered pair* to be a special kind of set containing exactly two elements, with the additional property that we are able to distinguish one of the elements, called the *first element*, from the other, called the *second element*. We shall designate such pairs (x, y), where x is the first element, and y is the second element. A fundamental principle of counting is the following:

If X and Y are any two sets with finitely many elements, the number of distinct ordered pairs (x, y) which can be formed with $x \in X$ and $y \in Y$ is $n(X)n(Y)$.

The concept of ordered pairs is easily extended to the concept of ordered r-tuples, each of which is a set with exactly r elements, with the property that it is possible to determine uniquely a first, second, . . . , rth element. Such r-tuples are denoted by $(x_1, x_2, \ldots, x_r)$. The fundamental principle extends to give the number of distinct r-tuples as the product of the numbers of elements which may be used for the respective positions.

DEFINITION. The number of *permutations of n things taken r at a time*, $0 \leq r \leq n$, is defined to be the number of distinct r-tuples which can be formed from n elements, where it is assumed that no element can simultaneously appear twice in one r-tuple. This number is denoted by $_nP_r$.

THEOREM 1. The value of $_nP_r$ is given by

$$_nP_r = n(n - 1)(n - 2) \cdots (n - r + 1). \tag{1}$$

Proof. If we consider the definition of $_nP_r$, it is clear that the first element of the r-tuple is to be chosen from a set of n elements. Having chosen the first element, a set of $n - 1$ elements is left, from which the second may be chosen, etc. Hence the formula follows.

In the case $r = n$, Theorem 1 says that there are $n(n - 1)(n - 2) \cdots (2)(1)$ permutations of n things taken n at a time. This number appears so often that it is convenient to give it a special designation, $n!$. We will extend the definition of this symbol to the special case $n = 0$ by defining $0!$ to be the number 1. Using this new notation, Eq. (1) can also be written as

$$_nP_r = \frac{n!}{(n - r)!} \quad \text{for} \quad r = 0, 1, 2, \ldots, n. \tag{2}$$

DEFINITION. The number of *combinations of n things taken r at a time* is defined to be the number of distinct subsets, each containing r elements, which are contained in a set with n elements. We denote this number by $\binom{n}{r}$.

THEOREM 2. The value of $\binom{n}{r}$ is given by

$$\binom{n}{r} = \frac{n!}{r!(n - r)!}. \tag{3}$$

Proof. Clearly the distinction between the numbers $_nP_r$ and $\binom{n}{r}$ is that $\binom{n}{r}$ counts subsets only, whereas $_nP_r$ counts each possible ordering within each subset. Hence the relation between the numbers is

$$_nP_r = r! \binom{n}{r}. \tag{4}$$

This follows since, after a subset has been chosen, it may still be arranged in $r!$ ways, by Theorem 1. If $_nP_r$ in Eq. (4) is replaced by $n!/(n - r)!$ and both sides of the resulting equation are divided by $r!$, Eq. (3) is obtained.

In any particular problem, before these formulas are used, care must be taken to determine whether permutations or combinations are required. Although no rules can be formulated to replace intelligent thinking, a guide to the correct choice is the decision as to whether "order" is important. In selecting a committee of three, where no significance is attached to being first, second, or third, it would be natural to use the idea of combinations. If, however, the first choice were to be chairman and the second choice secretary, it might be more natural to use the idea of permutations. That is, in this case we would consider the committee Jones, president; Smith, secretary; and Brown as distinct from the committee Brown, president; Smith, secretary; and Jones.

EXAMPLE 1. How many distinct numbers of four digits, each having no repeated digits, can be formed from the digits 1, 2, 3, 4, 5, 6, 7?

Solution. The number is $_7P_4 = 7!/3! = 840$.

EXAMPLE 2. How many different sums of money can be formed from one penny, one nickel, one dime, one quarter, and one half dollar?

Solution. Here order makes no difference, hence the answer is

$$\binom{5}{1} + \binom{5}{2} + \binom{5}{3} + \binom{5}{4} + \binom{5}{5} = 31,$$

allowing for sums involving 1, 2, 3, 4, or 5 coins.

EXAMPLE 3. Find the probability that a five-card poker hand will be a straight flush (five cards in sequence in a single suit, but not with ace high; the ace may be used as low card, however).

Solution. First, the choices of suit and of possible hands within a suit may be thought of as the choice of pairs of elements, the first from the class of suits, the second from the class of allowable hands within suits, and hence the basic principle of counting may be applied. There are four possible suits, and a permissible hand may have as low card any of the nine cards A, 2, 3, ..., 9. The total number of five-card hands (corresponding to the number of elements in the sample space) is $\binom{52}{5}$. Hence the desired probability is $(4)(9)/\binom{52}{5}$, or approximately 0.000,014.

EXERCISES

1. (a) How many distinct numbers of four digits each, with no repeated digits, can be formed from the digits 1, 2, 3, 4, and 5? (b) How many of these are even? (c) How many of the even numbers are larger than 3000?

2. How many straight lines are determined by ten points, no three of which lie on the same straight line?

3. How many different hands of five cards can be dealt from a bridge deck?

4. In how many ways can a set of six beads, each of a different color, be strung on a loop of string? Explain why this answer is different from the number of ways in which six people can be seated at a round table, and why both are different from the number of ways in which six people can be seated in a straight line.

5. In how many ways may a committee of three men and three women be selected from a group of six men and five women, one of whom is to be named chairman? (Consider two committees alike only if they contain the same members and have the same chairman.)

6. (a) What is the probability that a hand of five cards dealt from a bridge deck will contain two aces but no more? (b) What is this probability if it is

known that one of the five cards is the jack of clubs? (c) What is this probability if it is known that one of the five cards is an ace? (d) What is this probability if it is known that one of the five cards is the ace of spades?

7. Find the probability of obtaining each of the following poker hands in a five-card hand.

(a) Royal flush (A, K, Q, J, 10 in the same suit).
(b) Four of a kind (four cards with the same face value).
(c) Full house (three cards with one face value, two with another).
(d) Flush (five cards of the same suit but not in sequence).

8. Find an expression for the probability that a hand of five cards dealt from a bridge deck will contain three or more cards in numerical sequence in a single suit, and no card in the hand will be an ace.

9. What is the probability that the birthdays of twelve people will fall in twelve different calendar months? (Consider the probability that a birthday falls in any given month to be $\frac{1}{12}$, and assume that the events are independent.)

10. At a party, ten people place their shoes in a pile. Eight shoes are taken at random from the pile. What is the probability that among the eight shoes there is no complete pair?

7–5 Bernoulli trials, binomial distribution. If X and Y are two events in an arbitrary sample space, it is not generally true that $P(Y|X) = P(Y)$. That is, intuitively speaking, knowledge of the prior occurrence of X often implies information concerning the event Y and thus affects the probability of the occurrence of Y. There are certain cases, however, in which knowledge of one event does not give any information concerning a second event. For example, if a coin is tossed twice, knowing that the first toss resulted in heads does not help in any way in predicting what the result of the second toss will be. We refer to this situation by saying that the result of the second toss is independent of the result of the first toss.

In cases where $P(Y|X) = P(Y)$, Eq. (3), Section 7–3, reduces to the formula $P(XY) = P(X)\,P(Y)$. This suggests the following definition.

DEFINITION. Two events X and Y are said to be *independent* if the equation $P(XY) = P(X)\,P(Y)$ holds. Otherwise, X and Y are termed *dependent*.

EXAMPLE 1. The probability that a single card dealt from a bridge deck is an ace of spades is $\frac{1}{52}$, since the obvious sample space contains fifty-two points, of which only one is contained in the event "ace of spades is dealt." Note that if A is the event that the card is an ace, and S is the event that the card is spades,

$$P(A) = \tfrac{4}{52} = \tfrac{1}{13} \quad \text{and} \quad P(S) = \tfrac{1}{4}.$$

The event AS is the event that the card is an ace of spades. Then since

$$P(AS) = \tfrac{1}{52} = (\tfrac{1}{13})\,(\tfrac{1}{4}) = P(A)\,P(S),$$

it is seen that A and S are independent events.

The definition can be extended to include m events $X_1, X_2, \ldots, X_m$, but it is not quite so easy to justify this definition intuitively. We would like *independence* to mean that no information concerning the occurrence of any one or more of the m events affects the probability of any of the remaining events. This idea is made precise in the following definition.

DEFINITION. The events $X_1, X_2, \ldots, X_m$ are said to be *independent* provided that the probability of the joint occurrence of any r of the events, $2 \leq r \leq m$, equals the product of the r probabilities of the occurrence of the separate events.

As an illustration of the implications of this definition, we will prove the following theorem.

THEOREM 1. If the events A, B, and C are independent, then the events $A + B$ and C are independent.

Proof.

$$P[(A + B)C] = P(AC + BC) \qquad \text{by distributive law for sets}$$

$$= P(AC) + P(BC) - P(ABC)$$
$$\text{by Theorem 2 of Section 7-2}$$

$$= P(A)\, P(C) + P(B)\, P(C) - P(A)\, P(B)\, P(C)$$
$$\text{by definition of independence}$$

$$= [P(A) + P(B) - P(A)\, P(B)]\, P(C)$$
$$\text{by distributive law of numbers}$$

$$= [P(A) + P(B) - P(AB)]\, P(C)$$
$$\text{by definition of independence}$$

$$= P(A + B)\, P(C). \qquad \text{by Theorem 2 of Section 7-2}$$

But this represents the conditions that $A + B$ and C are independent events, which completes the proof.

The notion of independence of events will make possible a precise definition of repeated independent trials of an experiment. Intuitively, we think of performing an experiment over and over in such a way that the outcome of any particular trial is independent of all other trials. Examples of such trials are repeated tossings of a coin, repeated dealing of a five-card hand from a bridge deck, or weighing the wheat produced on each of several plots of ground planted under identical circumstances. To be precise, the definition can refer only to the sample space for the experiment, since the term *experiment* is not precisely defined.

DEFINITION. Let S be a sample space with sample points $P_1, P_2, \ldots, P_n$. By r independent trials corresponding to S, we mean the sample space whose points are all possible r-tuples $(P_{i_1}, P_{i_2}, \ldots, P_{i_r})$, where it is permissible for a given point P_j to appear more than once in a single r-tuple.

Even though the concept of independence of trials is not specifically stated in this definition, it follows from our definition of probability in a sample space. For example, consider two independent trials corresponding to a space with sample points X, Y, and Z. Independence of the first and second trials means that the probability of the pair (X, Z), for example, is equal to the product of the probabilities that X occurs at the first trial and Z occurs at the second. That this is the case is easily verified. Let A be the event that X occurs at trial 1, and B be the event that Z occurs at trial 2. Then AB is the event that both A and B occur. $P(AB)$ may be computed from the definition of repeated trials. The proper sample space contains nine points, of which only one corresponds to AB. Hence $P(AB) = \frac{1}{9}$. But $P(A) = \frac{1}{3}$ and $P(B) = \frac{1}{3}$. Hence $P(AB) = P(A) P(B)$, and the trials are independent.

DEFINITION. The term *Bernoulli trials* of an experiment will mean repeated trials of an experiment for which there are exactly two possible outcomes at each trial and such that the probabilities of these outcomes remain the same at each trial.

EXAMPLE 2. Consider the experiment consisting of rolling a die six times. If we are interested only in whether a single roll comes up 5, we may conceive of the experiment as Bernoulli trials with the two possible outcomes A (that 5 appears) and B (that 5 does not appear). $P(A) = \frac{1}{6}$ and $P(B) = \frac{5}{6}$. The probability that a 5 appears on each trial is therefore $(\frac{1}{6})^6$, because the trials are independent.

In referring to Bernoulli trials, it is customary to refer to one of the possible outcomes of any trial as *success*, and to the other as *failure*. A frequently occurring problem is that in which the number of successes in n trials is the only thing of interest, and not the order in which these successes occur. The probability of exactly k successes in n trials is given in the next theorem.

THEOREM 2. Let $b(k; n, p)$ denote the probability that n Bernoulli trials, with probability p for success and $q = 1 - p$ for failure at each trial, will result in k successes and $n - k$ failures $(0 \leq k \leq n)$. Then $b(k; n, p) = \binom{n}{k} p^k q^{n-k}$.

Proof. First consider the probability that the n trials will result in k successes and $n - k$ failures in any one fixed order. Independence of the trials implies that the probability of k successes and $n - k$ failures in this particular order is $p^k q^{n-k}$. The number of distinct orderings which will result in k successes is equal to the number of subsets of k elements contained in a set of n elements. Here the elements are the n numbered trials. That is, the number of orderings is $\binom{n}{k}$. Since these orderings correspond to mutually exclusive events (n trials cannot result simultaneously in two different orderings of successes and failures), the probabilities are additive. The probability $b(k; n, p)$ is therefore $\binom{n}{k} p^k q^{n-k}$, which completes the proof.

DEFINITION. The function $b(k; n, p)$ is called the *binomial distribution*.

EXAMPLE 3. In a certain college with 6000 students, one third of the students are girls. What is the probability that if a group of ten students is chosen at random, exactly three of them will be girls?

Solution. Selecting ten students does not strictly correspond to ten Bernoulli trials since if the first is a girl, for instance, the probability that the second is a girl is no longer $\frac{1}{3}$, but 1999/5999. However, considering the problem as Bernoulli trials, with $p = \frac{1}{3}$ and $q = \frac{2}{3}$, will give a very close approximation to the correct probability. This approximation is

$$b(3; 10, \tfrac{1}{3}) = \binom{10}{3} (\tfrac{1}{3})^3 (\tfrac{2}{3})^7 = 0.26, \quad \text{approximately.}$$

EXERCISES

1. What is the probability that, in six rolls of a single die, an ace will appear exactly twice?

2. What is the probability that, in tossing a coin ten times, (a) heads will occur exactly six times? (b) heads will occur at least six times?

3. What is the probability that, in rolling five dice at the same time, at least one will come up 6?

4. Suppose that in taking a multiple-choice test having ten questions, each with four possible answers, a student answers every problem by guessing. What is the probability that he will get a grade of 70% or better?

5. A pair of dice are rolled together ten times. Success on a roll of the dice will correspond to obtaining a sum of 7 on the two dice. (a) What is the probability of exactly three successes in the ten trials? (b) What is the probability of at least three successes in the ten trials?

6. All possible 3-digit numbers are formed from the digits 0, 1, 2, 3, 4, and 5, and each is written on a tag and placed in a bowl. (Note that numbers like 025, with 0 as first digit, are 2-digit numbers—not 3-digit.) Find the probability that a tag drawn at random from the bowl bears an even number.

7. Prove that if events A, B, C, and D are independent, then the events $A + B$ and $C + D$ are also independent.

REFERENCES

CRAMÉR, HARALD, *The Elements of Probability*, John Wiley and Sons, 1955.

FELLER, WILLIAM, *An Introduction to Probability Theory and Its Applications*, 2nd ed., John Wiley and Sons, 1957.

KEMENY, SNELL, and THOMPSON, *Finite Mathematics*, Prentice-Hall, 1957.

MUNROE, M. E., *Theory of Probability*, McGraw-Hill, 1951.

WHITWORTH, W. A., *Choice and Chance*, 5th ed., G. E. Stechert, New York, 1942.

ANSWERS TO SELECTED PROBLEMS

Section 1–3

1. (a) The set of all books written either in French or in German. (c) The set of all books written in German.

2. (a) The set consists of all yellow (French) books and all black books written in English.

3. (a) true   (c) true

5. (a) SM (c) EM

Section 1–4

2. (a)   (c)

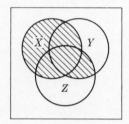
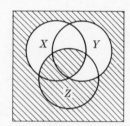

3. (a) valid   (c) valid   (e) invalid   (g) valid   (i) valid

4. (a) $X'Y'$ (c) $XYZ + X'Y'Z'$

Section 1–6

1. (a) X (c) $YZ + XZ$

2. (a) $(X + Y')(X + Z)$ (c) $(X + Y)(X + Z + W)$ (e) $A(X' + Y)$

3. (a) 0 (c) A (e) B (g) 0

4. (a) $A'B$ (c) $C(ABD)'$ (e) $AB + A'B' + C$ (g) XY (i) $X + Y$

Section 1–7

2. (a) $X'YZ' = 0$

3. (a) $X' + Y \subseteq Z + W'$ (c) $YZW \subseteq X$

7. A good student will receive a fine job.

Section 1–8

3. $X + AB' + A'B = 0$

7. (1) There are no witches in Moo. (2) Those who wear red feathers constitute the same set as those who are married.

Section 1–9

1. General solution: $AB' + A'B \subseteq X \subseteq B$. Eliminant: $AB' = 0$

3. General solution: $X = 0$. Eliminant: $0 = 0$

5. General solution: $BD' + B'D \subseteq X \subseteq AC + A'C'$. Eliminant: $(AC' + A'C)(BD' + B'D) = 0$

7. General solution: $X = 0$. Eliminant: $B = C$

Section 1-10

3. $n(G) \geqq n[G(S + F)] = n(GS + GF) = n(GS) + n(GF) - n(GFS) = 26$, whereas $n(G)$ is given as 25.

5. 55

Section 2-4

1. (a) $xy + xy' + x'y$ (c) $uv'w + u'vw' + uv'w'$
   (e) $xyzt + x'y'zt + xy'z't$

3. (a) $xyz + xyz' + xy'z + xy'z' + x'y'z + x'y'z'$
   (c) $xy'z + x'yz + xy'z' + x'yz'$

5. $xyz' + xy'z$ 7. $f_1 = xz'$

Section 2-5

1. (a) $x + y$
   (c) $(u + v + w)(u + v + w')(u + v' + w')(u' + v' + w)(u' + v' + w')$
   (g) $(x + z)(x + z')(x' + z)$

3. (a) $(x + y' + z)(x + y' + z')$
   (c) $(x + y + z)(x + y + z')(x' + y' + z)(x' + y' + z')$

6. (a) $u' + v$ 7. (a) $x'y'$

Section 3-2

1. (a) yes   (c) no   (e) yes

2. (a) Mathematics is easy and 2 is less than 3. (c) That mathematics is easy and that 2 is less than 3 are not both true.

3. (a) $p + q$ (c) $pq + p'q'$

4. (a) Either ice is not cold or I am not tired. (c) Oranges are suitable for use in vegetable salads.

5. (a) false   (c) true   (e) false   (g) false   (i) true

6. (a) always false   (c) sometimes true, sometimes false

Section 3-3

1. (a) tautology   (c) tautology

3. $F_1 = p'q + r$, $F_3 = pq + p'q'r$, $F_5 = p' + q'$

5. (a), (c)

p	q	r	$pqr + p'qr' + p'q'r'$	$(p' + qr)'(pq + q'r)$
1	1	1	1	0
1	1	0	0	1
1	0	1	0	1
1	0	0	0	0
0	1	1	0	0
0	1	0	1	0
0	0	1	0	0
0	0	0	1	0

Section 3-6

1. (a) 1, 2, 4, 5, 7, 9   (c) 1, 2, 3, 4, 5, 6, 7, 9, 10

3. Yes. It is impossible that both statements be true, and impossible that both be false.

7. (a)   (c)

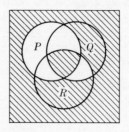

Section 3-7

1. (a) Some man is wealthy. (c) No man is wealthy.

2. (a) Some real numbers are greater than 7. (c) For every real number, there is another number such that the sum of the two is 7.

3. (a) At least one American is not crazy. (c) No person is happy all the time. (e) There is at least one pair of triangles for which the corresponding sides are equal and yet the triangles are not congruent.

Section 3-8

3. (a) invalid   (c) valid   (e) invalid   (g) valid

4. (a) invalid   (c) valid

5. Yes. He did not take soup.

Section 3-10

3. $p \rightarrow q = p \downarrow (p \downarrow q)$

5. (a) neither p nor q. (c) $p' = p \uparrow p$, $pq = (p \uparrow p) \uparrow (q \uparrow q)$

6. (a)

p	q	$p \pm q$
1	1	0
1	0	1
0	1	1
0	0	0

(c) yes

Section 3-11

1. No gray ducks in this village wear lace collars.

3. *Hint:* Show that the rules are inconsistent by reducing the set of rules to a single rule in the form 1 = 0.

5. One

Section 4–2

2. (a)

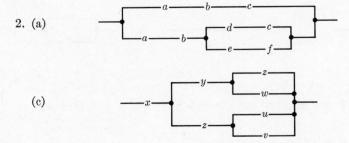

(c)

3. (a) $(a + b)[cde + (f + g)h]$ (c) $u[v(y + x(z + t)) + ws(x + y)]$

4. (a)

7.

a	b	c	Circuit
1	1	1	0
1	1	0	1
1	0	1	0
1	0	0	0
0	1	1	0
0	1	0	0
0	0	1	0
0	0	0	1

8. Circuit to realize f_1:

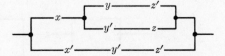

Section 4-3

1. —c—   3. —a'——b—   5.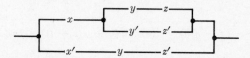

Section 4-4

1. $a(b + c)$ 2. $x(y + z)$ 4. (a) $a'(x + bc'y) + w(c' + x + ab + ay)$

Section 4-5

1. Circuit to realize f using eight contacts:

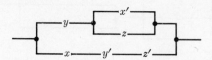

Circuit to realize h using 1 in row 5, 0 in row 7 (six contacts):

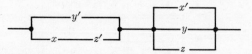

Circuit to realize h using 0 in row 5, 1 in row 7 (six contacts):

5. Series-parallel circuit:

Section 4-6

1.

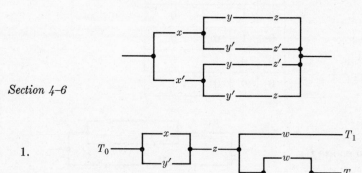

3.

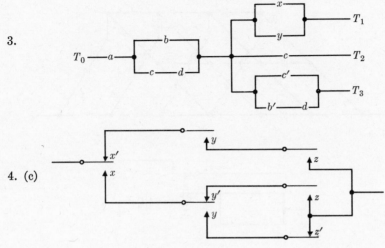

4. (c)

Section 4-7

1.

or T_1

3.

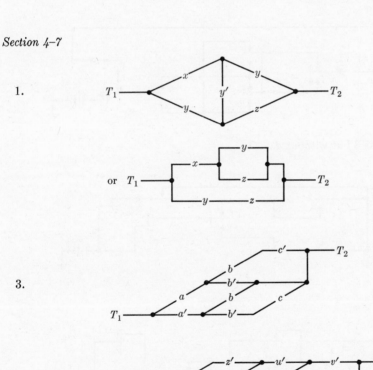

5.

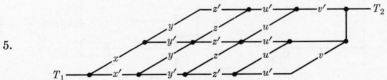

7

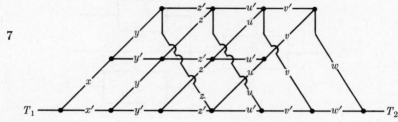

Section 5-2

1.

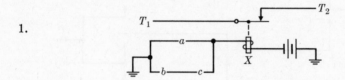

3.

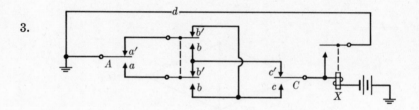

5. Same as 3 but without *d*.

7.

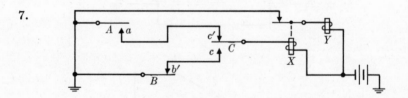

Section 5-3

1.

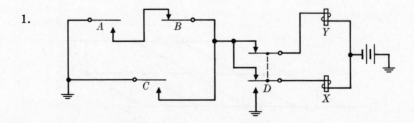

3.

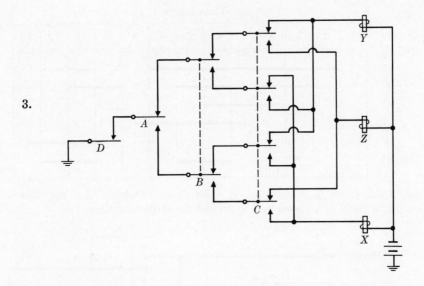

Section 5–4

1. $F_x = b'c + a'bc' + x$ with the following circuit:

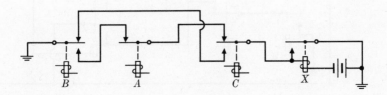

3.

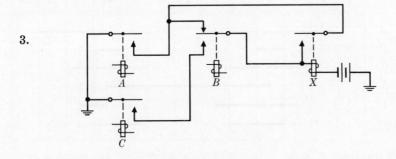

Section 5–6

2. (a)

	Time interval												
	1	2	3	4	5	6	7	8	9	10	11	12	13

A

B

C

X

Y

Output

Control functions: $f_x = cb' + ax$, $f_y = ba' + ay$. Output: $bx + ay$, where the output is given as a closed lead to ground for these conditions.

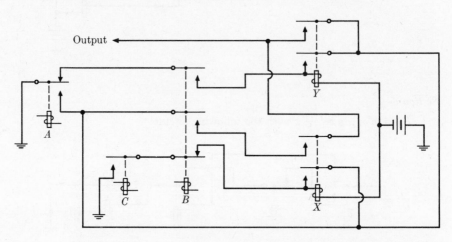

3.

	Time interval												
	1	2	3	4	5	6	7	8	9	10	11	12	13

A

B

C

X

Y

Output

Control functions: $f_x = by + (y + b')x$, $f_y = b'cx' + cy$. Output: $b + cx$

Section 6–2

1. (a) 100,111,101   (c) 2232   (e) 475
2. (a) 45   (c) 1200
4. (a) 100,000   (c) 1,111,101   (e) 0.0001
5. (a) 47   (c) 33   (e) 3.25
6. (a) 1,101.01   (c) 11.0010

Section 7–2

1. (a) $\frac{2}{5}$ (c) $\frac{1}{10}$
3. (a) $\frac{1}{2}$ (c) $\frac{2}{3}$ (e) $\frac{1}{6}$
4. (a) $\frac{1}{4}$ (c) $\frac{3}{14}$
7. (a) 0.70   (c) 0.90   (e) 0.05   (g) 0.50

Section 7–3

1. (a) $\frac{1}{6}$ (b) $\frac{1}{3}$
3. (a) $\frac{8}{19}$ (c) $\frac{1}{5}$
5. $\frac{7}{20}$
7. $\frac{3}{4}$

Section 7–4

1. (a) 120   (c) 30
3. $\binom{52}{5} = 2,598,960$
5. 1200
6. (a) $\binom{48}{3}\binom{4}{2}/\binom{52}{5}$ (b) $\binom{4}{2}\binom{47}{2}/\binom{51}{4}$
7. (a) $4/\binom{52}{5}$ (c) $3744/\binom{52}{5}$
10. $\binom{10}{8}2^8/\binom{20}{8}$

Section 7–5

1. $b(2; 6, \frac{1}{6}) = \binom{6}{2}(\frac{1}{6})^2(\frac{5}{6})^4$
3. $1 - (\frac{5}{6})^5$
5. (a) $b(3; 10, \frac{1}{6}) = \binom{10}{3}(\frac{1}{6})^3(\frac{5}{6})^7$

INDEX

When a reference is to a problem, the problem number appears in parentheses following the page number.